Chess Workbook for Children

The Chess Detective's Introduction to the Royal Game

TODD BARDWICK

Chess Detective Press

Illustrations by Kevin Hempstead

Chess Workbook for Children
The Chess Detective's Introduction to the Royal Game

First printing: July 2006

www.ColoradoMasterChess.com

ISBN-10: 0-9761962-1-2
ISBN-13: 978-0-9761962-1-1

Library of Congress Control Number: 2006903602

Library of Congress Cataloging-in-Publication Data available upon request

DEDICATION

This book is dedicated to chess students everywhere with the sincerest wish that chess will enrich your life in whatever endeavors you choose to pursue in the future.

Have fun learning how to play the Royal Game!

CONTENTS

INTRODUCTION FOR PARENTS

Chess has been the ultimate game of strategy for generations. Played by adults and children for centuries as a fun and entertaining way to challenge the mind, chess is one of the most popular games in the world.

Benjamin Franklin wrote in 1779 that the game of chess "is not merely an idle amusement (since) life is a kind of chess, in which we have often points to gain, and competitors or adversaries to contend with, and in which there is a vast variety of good and evil events that are in some degree the effects of prudence or the want of it." Franklin suggested that playing chess develops foresight, circumspection, perseverance, and sportsmanship.

Today, educators and parents have discovered that chess is a wonderful way to teach young children mathematical concepts and important thinking skills they can use their entire life.

Here is a summary of some benefits of learning to play chess:
- Improves cognitive skills (including concentration, pattern recognition, decision making, algebraic and geometric thinking, problem-solving, spatial reasoning, and critical-thinking skills)
- Improves self-confidence and self-worth
- Increases attention span
- Increases memory capacity
- Encourages understanding of choice and consequences for problem-solving - helps students realize that they are responsible for their actions and must accept the consequences of those actions
- Provides competition, fosters interest and promotes mental alertness
- Teaches good sportsmanship
- Improves communication through written and oral presentation skills

Many studies (see www.uschess.org) show chess helps children with cognitive development and increases math and verbal test scores. Educators have also noted chess helps to raise self-esteem.

Chess also lays a solid foundation for the student's real-world business success later in life and overlaps strategies used in the world of sports.

Time-management skills, in particular, are developed through chess. The chess player has a limited amount of time to complete the game and must budget this time carefully by picking the correct points in the game to spend his thinking time. As in life, and in the classroom when taking tests, the student needs to learn how to use his time efficiently.

A chess problem also forces the student to look at both sides of a situation. This is a breakthrough concept for most young children who are mainly focused on themselves. In chess, a young student learns that his opponent's moves and pieces are just as important as his own. Debating skills, where the debater must consider both sides of an argument, are developed through chess. Both time-management skills and the ability to assess a problem from different perspectives are critical for attorneys, businessmen, and salesmen.

From a pure calculation perspective, chess can help develop logical and critical-thinking skills needed for engineering, which I can personally attest to as a civil engineer.

You will definitely observe that children who are good at math also tend to be good chess players. Most good math students will pick up chess quickly. Chess is also an effective teaching tool for the students who have difficulty with math, because it teaches math concepts in the context of a game, making it more fun and interesting.

Chess Workbook for Children is designed as a companion workbook to the teacher's book, *Teaching Chess in the 21st Century – Strategies and Connections to a Standards-Based World. Teaching Chess in the 21st Century* outlines a beginner chess course for classroom use by the teacher and compares chess with a sample 2nd grade math curriculum, emphasizing the overlap with National Council of Teachers of Mathematics Standards.

The same ten basic chess lessons from *Teaching Chess in the 21st Century* are presented in this workbook. Both of these books can stand on their own or be used together and contain real-life analogies that children will easily relate to.

At the end of each lesson in the workbook, there are two problem sets of varying difficulty - Basset Hound problems are the easiest; the Chess Detective problems are tougher.

Finally, I would like to thank the people who helped make *Chess Workbook for Children* a success.

First, to my students over the years who helped to develop the stories presented here and for giving me the opportunity to gain experience as to how to effectively present a chess curriculum to children.

For proofreading and making suggestions on how to improve the book, I would like to thank my father, Alan Bardwick, an Expert strength tournament player and retired business professor at the Community College of Aurora; Richard Cordovano, a software engineer, Class B strength tournament player, and part-time chess coach; and Gary Bagstad, a middle school teacher in Denver Public Schools, Class A/B strength tournament player, and school chess coach.

I greatly appreciate the time and effort from Gordon Pierce for his advice and consultation in educating me about the details of the publishing industry.

Finally, I would like to thank the artist, Kevin Hempstead, for the clever and entertaining illustrations that he created for the book.

Best wishes in your chess endeavors,

Todd Bardwick
National Chess Master

INTRODUCTION FOR CHILDREN

Chess is the ultimate strategy game and lots of fun! This is a workbook for children who are learning how to play chess. Reading all the chapters should be easy and fun; you will enjoy the stories and the large chess diagrams. You may want to have a chess set nearby to play out some of the moves that are in the workbook.

The glossary in the back of the book gives a quick reference for chess terms and words that you may not know. Throughout the chapters of the book, the first time more difficult words are used their definitions will be given in brackets [   ] after the word.

At the end of each chapter, you can test your new chess skills with two groups of problems.

If you are brand new to chess, start with the Basset Hound problems.

Intermediate students can move on and try the Chess Detective problems.

The answers to the problems are in Appendix B in the back of the book.

Check out the chess crossword puzzles and word searches in Appendix A.

Have fun!

LESSON 1

CHESS BASICS

"You sit at the board and suddenly your heart leaps. Your hand trembles to pick up the piece and move it. But what chess teaches you is that you must sit there calmly and think about whether it's really a good idea and whether there are other, better ideas."

Stanley Kubrick (1928-1999)
filmmaker, producer

Chess started in India hundreds of years ago and is played all over the world today. It is an easy game to learn, but a tough game to master! If you have never played before, this lesson will teach you the basics.

There are pawns and five types of pieces in a game of chess. Each has different moves and powers. There are white pieces and black pieces.

Here are the names of the pieces and their symbols:

King	K	♔	♚
Queen	Q	♕	♛
Rook	R	♖	♜
Bishop	B	♗	♝
Knight	N	♘	♞
Pawn	P	♙	♟

The battlefield for a chess game is called a chessboard. Each army starts out with the same eight pieces and eight pawns.

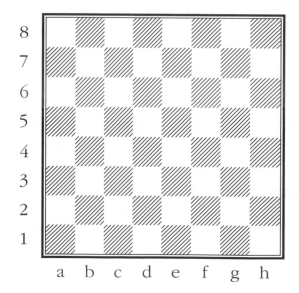

A chessboard has 64 squares.

If you are good at multiplication, you will notice that 8 x 8 = 64. (8 squares top to bottom and 8 squares left to right)

32 squares are white (or light) and 32 squares are black (or dark).

The lower right hand square for each player is white. To help you remember how the board is rotated there is a famous chess saying, "White on Right."

2

Each square has a first and a last name. The square's first name is a small letter, and its last name is a number. If you have ever played the game *Battleship*, the naming system is similar.

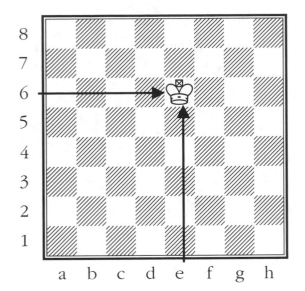

The White king is on e6.

The Black king is on a2.
The White knight is on g7.
The White pawn is on f3.
The Black queen is on e1.
The Black bishop is on b7.
The White rook is on c5.

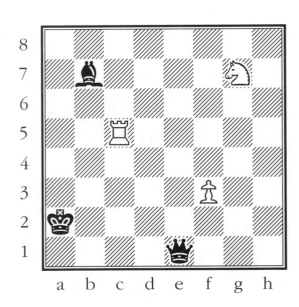

Ranks and Files

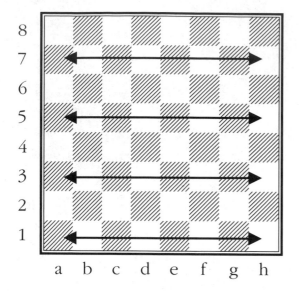 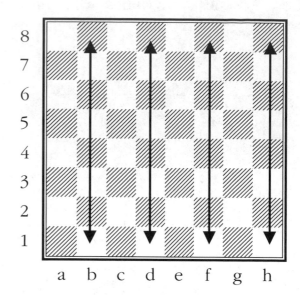

Ranks are rows.
The ranks are named 1 through 8.

Files are columns.
The files are named a through h.

Ranks are numbered from each player's side, starting with the 1st rank closest to the player. The 8th rank is defined as the rank furthest away from the player. In other words, on the diagram at the bottom of page 3, the Black king on a2 is on White's 2nd rank, which is Black's 7th rank.

Piece Movements, Captures and Values

Each piece moves in a special way and has its own value. Neither player can capture his own pieces. The following pages show how the pawns and each of the chess pieces move. White and Black take turns moving.

King

The king can only move one square at time in any direction. You can only have one king (unlike checkers) and he is worth the entire game and cannot be traded. Pretend he is valuable because he is carrying all the gold of the kingdom, and he is slow, because gold is heavy! Your opponent wants to capture the king and take away his gold.

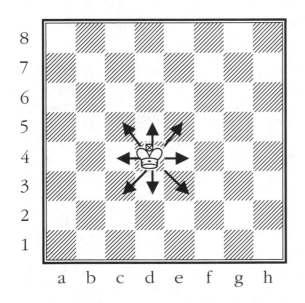

The king can move one square in any direction.

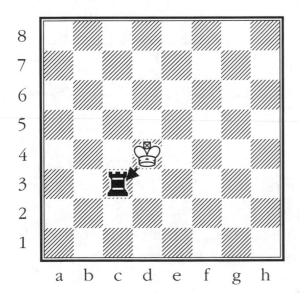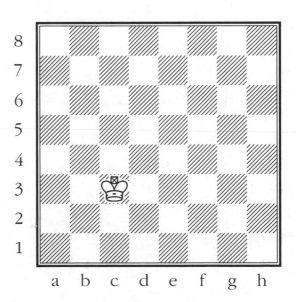

A King can capture a piece on any square next to him. He captured the rook on c3.

Pawn

The Pawn can move either one square or two squares forward, but only if no piece is blocking its path. It can only move two squares forward if it is on its starting square. Pawns are the only piece that cannot move backwards. Each player begins the game with eight pawns.

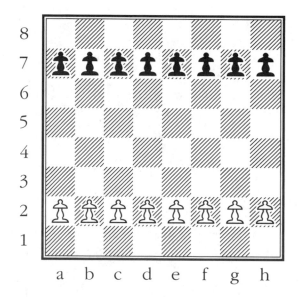

Starting position for the pawns.

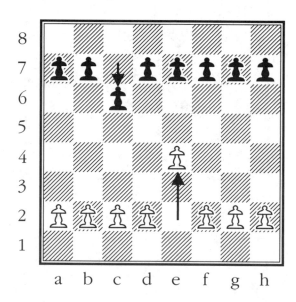

White's pawn moves forward two squares. Black's pawn moves one square forward.

The pawn is the only piece that captures differently than it moves. Pawns capture one square forwards in a diagonal direction. When chess was invented many years ago, the pawn was a foot soldier, holding a shield in front of him, for protection. The soldier would stab at his opponent diagonally out to the front, not directly forwards because his shield would block his sword.

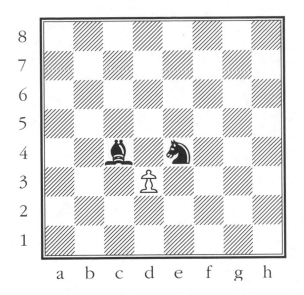

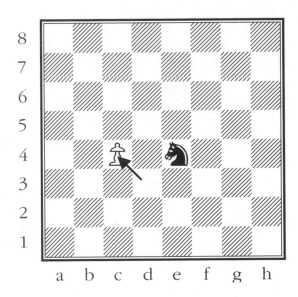

The White pawn can either move to d4, capture the bishop, or capture the knight.

The pawn captured the bishop.

The first special move in chess is when the pawn gets to the eighth rank (and scores a touchdown!); it promotes into a queen, rook, bishop, or knight.

The queen is usually selected as the promotion piece because she is the most powerful. Usually pawns promote at the end of the game since this is when the opponent has the fewest pieces available for defense. The greatest number of queens possible in a game for either player is nine (you start the game with one queen and eight pawns). Two queens is usually all you need.

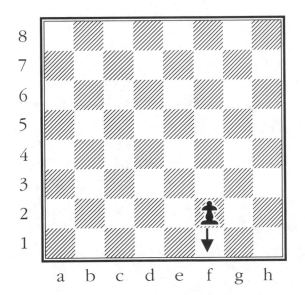

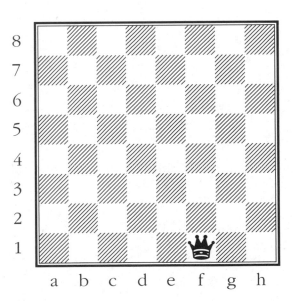

The Black pawn moves forward and promotes to a queen.

Pawns have the lowest value of any piece and are worth one, or one pawn.

Knight

The knight looks like a horse and is the only piece that can jump over other pieces. Knights move in a capital "L" shape, two squares in one direction, then one square to either side.

On each move, the knight changes the color of its square from light to dark or from dark to light. A knight can move to every square on the board, but is a slow-moving piece.

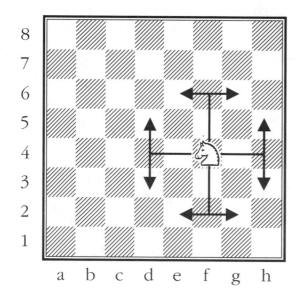

The knight can move to eight squares, e2, g2, h3 ,h5, g6, e6, d5, or d3.

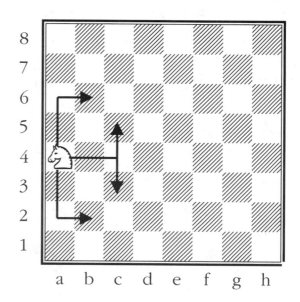

A knight on the rim can only move to four squares: b2, c3, c5 or b6.

Knights capture by landing on an opponent's piece, not by jumping over it. If a horse jumps over your head, you are okay. If a horse lands on your head, you are *not* okay!

Because knights are slow-moving pieces, they like to be located near the center of the board so that they can move to any part of the board quickly. A knight on the edge of the board takes several moves to get to the other side of the board. There is an old chess rhyme, "A knight on the rim is dim." The rim is the outer edge of the board and dim means bad or weak. A knight is worth three pawns or three points.

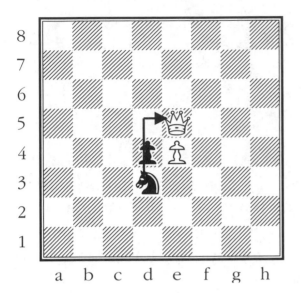 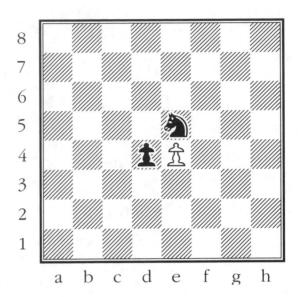

The Black knight jumps over the pawns and captures the White queen on e5.

Bishop

The bishop has a pointed or "diagonal-shaped" head that looks like a miter, the hat worn by a bishop (a high-ranking Christian clergyman). The bishop moves diagonally and is a fast-moving, long-range piece. It cannot jump over pieces like a knight. Each bishop is limited to only one color, or 32 squares. At the start of the game, each player has a bishop that can move on light squares and one that can move on dark squares.

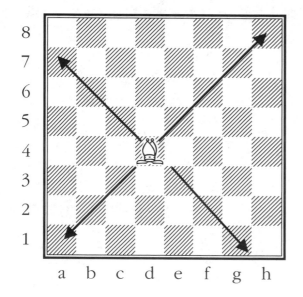

Bishops can move to any square along a diagonal. Unlike the knight, a bishop cannot jump over other pieces.

Bishops and knights are called minor pieces. Comparing the two, the knight has the advantage of being able to touch each of the 64 squares, but is slow. The bishop is fast, but can only touch 32 squares. These powers tend to balance each other out. Bishops are equal to knights in strength, and are also worth three pawns.

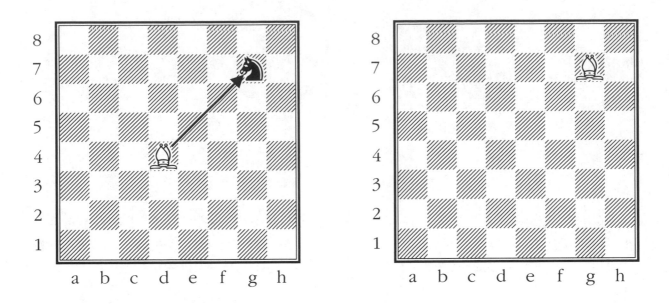

The bishop on d4 captures the knight on g7.

Rook

Rooks move horizontally [left or right] and vertically [up or down] like the cutout portion of the top of the castle on their head. Rooks are fast-moving, long-range pieces that can move to all 64 squares. Rooks, like bishops, cannot jump.

Comparing a rook to a knight, both can move to any of the 64 squares, but the rook is fast and the knight is slow. Therefore, the rook is more valuable than the knight.

Comparing a rook to a bishop, both are fast. The rook can move to any of the 64 squares, while the bishop is limited to 32 squares. Again, the rook has the advantage. The rook is worth five pawns.

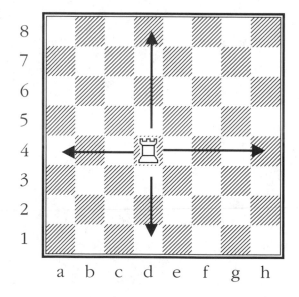

Rooks can move to any square forwards, backwards, left, or right.

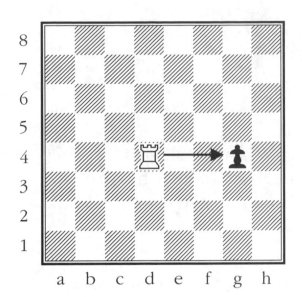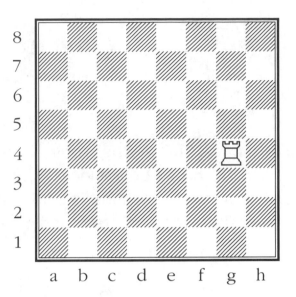

The rook captures the pawn on g4.

Queen

The queen moves horizontally and vertically like a rook, and diagonally like a bishop. She is both pieces rolled into one! The queen has a crown that points out in all directions (a clue to how she moves) and is worth nine pawns.

Queens and rooks are called major pieces.

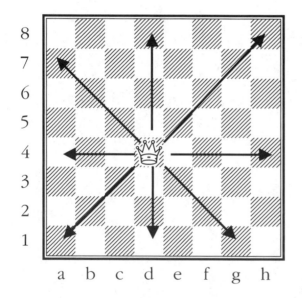

Queens are a combination of the rook and bishop, all rolled into one piece.

Because the queen is most powerful piece, most of the time when a pawn is promoted, it is promoted to a queen. When the pawn isn't promoted to a queen, a knight is typically chosen because a knight moves differently than a queen, which may prove useful in certain situations.

If your queen has been captured, you can place the captured queen back on the board on the square where the pawn promotes. If the original queen is still on the board, and a pawn promotes to give a player a second queen, either flip a captured rook upside down or borrow a queen from another chess set. A pawn placed on its side or two pawns crisscrossed on their side (so they don't roll around) can also represent a promoted queen.

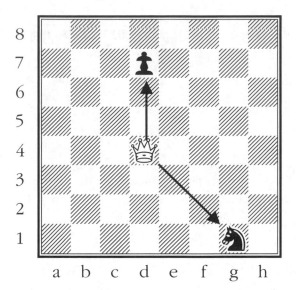

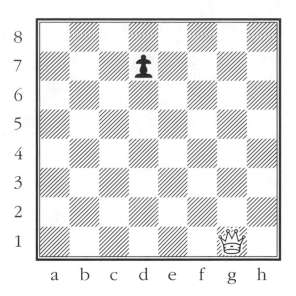

The queen can capture either the pawn or the knight.

She captures the knight.

Trading Pieces

Now that we know what the pieces are worth, it is easy to decide what is a good trade…just do the math!

Here are the piece values again:

pawn = 1
knight = 3
bishop = 3
rook = 5
queen = 9
king - cannot be traded

Would you trade a rook for a bishop and a knight? Yes, since 5 is less than 3 + 3 = 6. It is almost always a good idea to trade a piece of lesser value for a piece or pieces of greater value.

How about two rooks for a queen? No, because 10 is greater than 9.

Would you trade a bishop for three pawns? Maybe, since they are both worth three points.

If you have more points than your opponent, you have what is called a material advantage. It is normally a good idea to trade equal value pieces when you have a lead in material because with less total pieces on the board, the game is simpler and usually easier to win.

Check

Check occurs when a king is attacked by an opposing piece. The rules of chess state that when a player attacks the king and puts him in check, his opponent MUST make a move to escape the check. There are three possible ways to escape check: capture the checking piece, block the check by interposing [put in between] one of your pieces, or move the king to a square that isn't attacked.

You don't have to say "check". You are not allowed to capture kings. If a player's king is in check after he moves, he made an illegal move. He must then undo the illegal move and make a move that gets his king out of check.

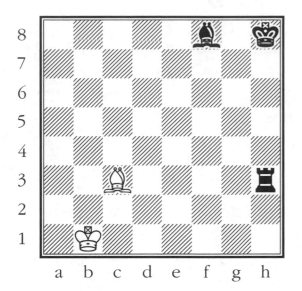
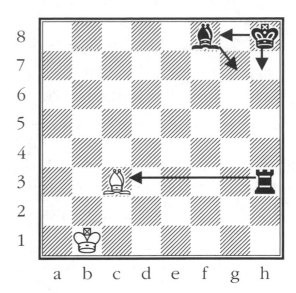

Black's king is in check from the bishop on c3. Black can *move* the king to g8 or h7, *interpose* with the bishop by playing …Bg7, or *capture* the bishop with the rook. Capturing the bishop is the best move because Black would gain three points.

Checkmate

Checkmate is when the king is in check, and there is no way to escape the check by moving the king to a safe square, blocking the check with a piece, or capturing the piece that checks the king. The object of the game is to put your opponent's king in checkmate.

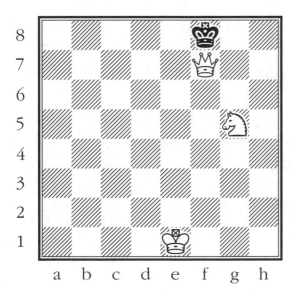

In this position, Black is checkmated. The White queen is attacking the Black king, putting him in check. The king cannot move safely to e8, e7, g8, or g7 because the White queen also attacks these squares. The Black king cannot capture the White queen because the White knight protects her and would then capture the king. Because the Black king is in check and has no way to escape check, he is checkmated. The game is over and White has won.

17

"Touch move" and "Touch take" rules

"Touch move" means that if you touch a piece, you have to move it - if you can move it legally. "Touch take" means that if you touch an opponent's piece, you must take it - if the piece can be legally captured. Finally, a move is completed when you take your hand off the piece.

These rules are all strictly enforced in chess tournaments. It is best to think with your head, not your fingers! If you have a problem touching the pieces, sit on your hands or put them in your pockets.

If one of the pieces is not centered on its square, the player whose move it is can say, "I adjust," and then center the piece on the correct square. The player must say, "I adjust," before touching the piece to undo the "touch move" rule. The "touch move" and "touch take" rules are like table manners at dinner. Do your parents allow you to touch all the pieces of bread on a plate at the dinner table. No! You have to eat the piece you touch. This table manners rule would be called "touch eat!"

Starting position for a new game

The board is set up the same way for every game, with a white square in the lower right hand corner of the board. Remember the chess saying, "White on Right."

White's pieces always start on rows 1 and 2. Black's pieces line up symmetrically [the mirror image] on the other side of the board on rows 7 and 8. On the back rank, the pieces are lined up with the tallest (king and queen) in the center and the shortest (rooks) in the corners. The height of the pieces decreases as you go from the center to the corner.

The queen starts on her own color; the White queen on a white square (d1) and the Black queen on a black square (d8). You can also think of it as the White queen wears a white dress and the Black queen wears a black dress.

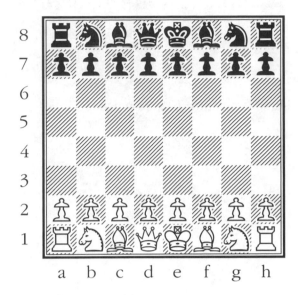

Starting position for a new game. White always moves first.

Basset Hound Problems

 1-1

How many points (pawns) are these White pieces worth?

___ + ___ + ___ + ___ = ____

 1-2

How many points are these Black pieces worth?

___ + ___ + ___ + ___ + ___ + ___ = _____

 1-3

What squares are the White pieces on?

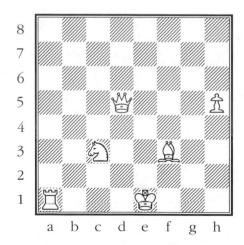

King ____		**Bishop** ____	
Queen ____		**Knight** ____	
Rook ____		**Pawn** ____	

 1-4

What squares are the Black pieces on?

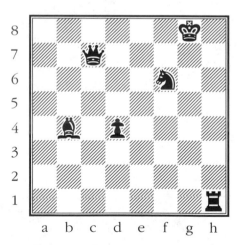

King ____		**Bishop** ____	
Queen ____		**Knight** ____	
Rook ____		**Pawn** ____	

1-5

 # 1-6

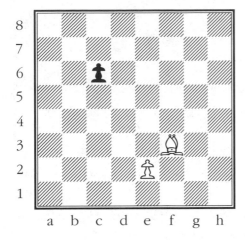

What squares can the bishop move to?

____, ____, ____, ____, ____, ____, ____

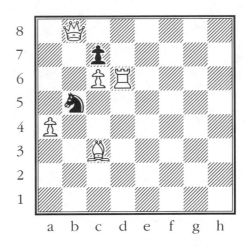

What pieces can the knight capture?

_____ _____

 # 1-7

1-8

Which piece is checking the Black king?

_____

Is White in checkmate? Why?

_____ , _____

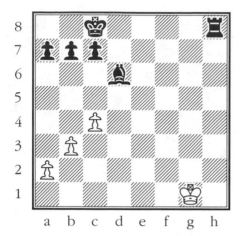

It is White's move and he touched his king. What are his legal moves?

_____, _____, _____

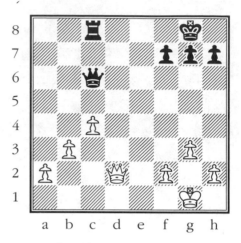

It is Black's move. He picks up the White pawn on c4 and then puts it back down. What move must he make?

_____

Chess Detective Problems

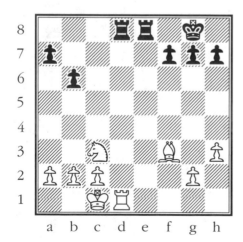

Who has more material? How much more?

_____, _____

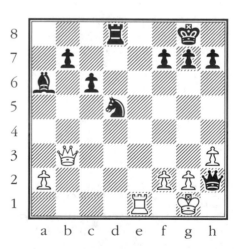

After White's next move, who will have more material? How much more?

_____, _____

 1-13

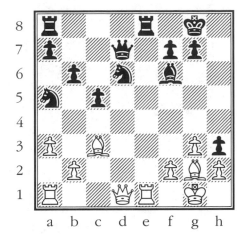

What is the most valuable piece White can capture with a bishop? What square is it on?

_____, _____

 1-14

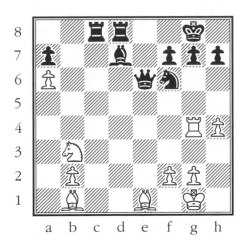

What is the total value of all the pieces the Black queen is attacking?

_____

 1-15

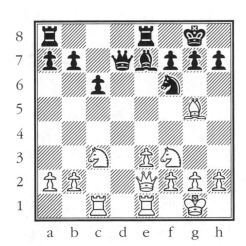

It is White's move. Is it a good move to trade the bishop for the knight? Why?

_____

 1-16

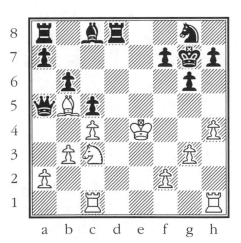

List all of the moves that Black can make to put the White king in check.

_____

 **1-17**

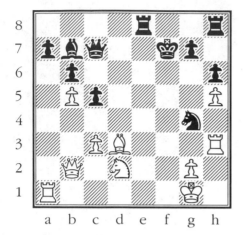

List all the moves that White can
make to put the Black king in check.

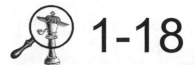 **1-18**

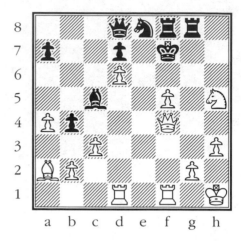

Is Black in checkmate? Why?

 1-19

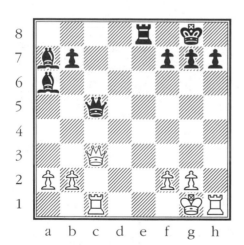

With White to move, he touches his king
and then says, "I adjust." Is he allowed
to capture the Black queen? Why?

 1-20

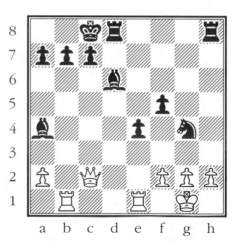

With Black to move, he touches the
White pawn on g2. Is he allowed to
capture White's queen? Why?

LESSON 2

OPENINGS

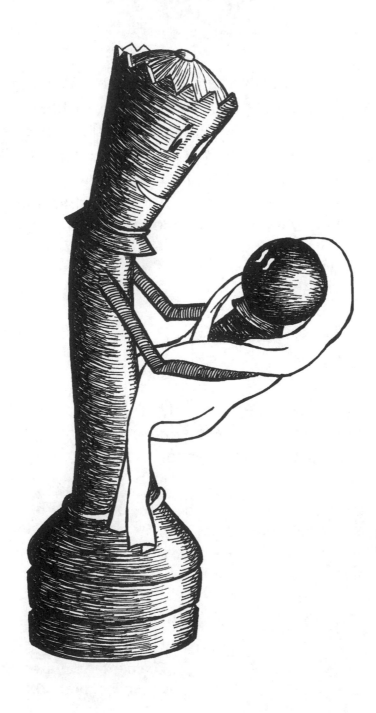

"Once a pawn a time..."

Every chess game starts with the same position. White always moves first; after that, the two players alternate taking turns for the rest of the game. In master games, White has an advantage because he has the first move. However, for beginners, having the first move is only a very slight advantage.

The opening is typically the first eight to ten moves of the game. Although thousands of books have been written on chess openings, all you need to know about the opening when you are learning to play is the basic principles:

- Control the center
- Develop your pieces
- Castle early

Control the center

The squares in the center (e4, e5, d4, and d5) are the most important on the board. By gaining control of these squares, you control more of the board and can launch an attack in any direction. Try to control the center squares with pawns and protect the pawns with your pieces. The squares on the edge of the board, or the rim, are the least important.

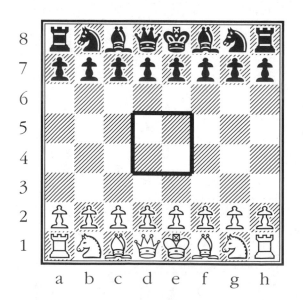

The center squares are e4, e5, d4, and d5.

Develop your pieces

Developing a piece means moving the piece off its starting square to a better square, usually toward the center of the board. The pieces you want to develop early are the knights and bishops. Remember that pawns are usually not called pieces and don't need to be developed.

Develop your pieces quickly and efficiently so that each piece can get toward the center of the board in the least number of moves possible. Develop the minor pieces (knights and bishops) first, and then the major pieces (rooks and queens). Try not to block the diagonals of the bishops with pawns. The rooks want to move to open files (files not blocked by your pawns).

Do not bring out your queen too early. If she enters the game too quickly, an experienced player will develop his pieces and attack the queen at the same time, forcing her to move again and waste time. If the player who brought the queen out early isn't looking at his opponent's threats, the queen usually gets captured quickly.

Castle early

Castling is the second of the special moves (promoting a pawn was the first). This is the only time that two pieces (king and rook) can be moved in one turn. A player can only castle once per game.

Castling allows you to safeguard the king by getting him out of the center of the board and to develop the rook by bringing the rook toward the center and into the game.

Try not to push pawns forward in front of a castled king because this opens up space in front of him, making him more open to attack. Remember that pawns cannot move backwards later to defend the important squares in front of the king.

The king hides near the edge of board, out of the action for most of the game. However, the king is a powerful piece. The time to centralize the king is in the endgame (when most of the pieces are captured), because he is not likely to get checkmated when there are only a few pieces left on the board.

How to castle

You can castle on either the kingside or the queenside. The kingside is the side of the board where the kings start out the game (e-h files). The queenside is the side where the queens begin the game (a-d files).

In order to castle kingside, the king knight and king bishop must move first so that the squares between the king and rook are open. When castling, you must touch the king first because of the "touch move" rule (moving the rook first would be a complete, legal rook move). First, move the king two squares to the g-file (g1 for White and g8 for Black) and then, with the same hand, pick up the rook and put it on the f-file (f1 for White and f8 for Black).

To castle queenside, the queen, queen bishop, and queen knight, must first be moved off of their starting squares. After that, pick up the king and move it two squares to the c-file (c1 for White and c8 for Black) and then, with the same hand, pick up the rook and put it on the d-file square (d1 for White and d8 for Black).

A simple way to remember this is that king moves two squares when castling on either side and the rook jumps over him.

Besides having all the pieces cleared out so that the king can "see" the rook, it is also a requirement that the *king has not already moved in the game* and that the *rook that he is castling with also has not previously moved*.

You are also *not allowed to castle to escape check, castle through check, or castle into check*.

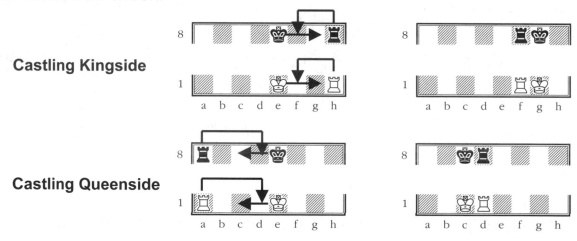

Castling Kingside

Castling Queenside

The diagrams on the next page show a position before castling, with both sides castled kingside, and with White castled on the queenside and Black castled on the kingside. In a real game, each player has the choice of which side to castle on, or to not castle at all. You can only castle once in the game.

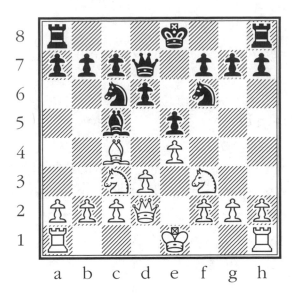

Position before castling.

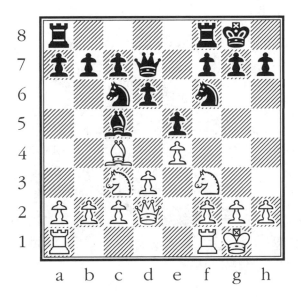

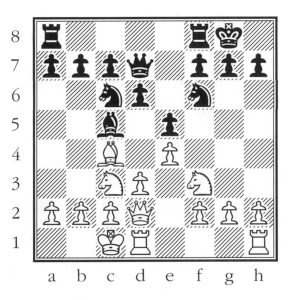

In this position, both players castled kingside.

Here, White castled queenside and Black castled kingside.

Opening Presents, A Story for Chess Openings

Here is a fun and easy story to help you remember the basic opening principles.

What happens on Christmas morning? You open presents. There are presents for the entire family. In chess, the pieces and pawns are the family members. Every time a piece moves, that piece opens a present and is happy. The goal of the opening is to have a happy family!

Let's identify the family members. The king is your dad, the queen is your mom, the knights and bishops are the younger brothers and sisters, the rooks are the teenagers, and the pawns are the babies. A big family!

Who opens their presents first? The young children. What pieces are they? The bishops and the knights.

Is it a good idea to make a lot of king moves? No...that is like the dad opening his presents first, while everyone else watches.

How about queen moves? No. That is like the mom opening her presents first, while the children watch.

What about pawns? In real life, babies can open presents, but babies are too young to know what presents are…so the pawns won't be unhappy if the young children (the knights and bishops) go first!

The rooks (teenagers) usually let the younger children go first.

The knights can open a present on the first move, because they can jump. What about the bishops? Bishops can't move on the first move of the game, because the pawns block them. There are babies on their presents. What do you have to do first if there is a baby on the present? Move the baby!

Notice that there are four children, two knights and two bishops, that want to open their presents first. Remember the goal is to create as much happiness as you can in the family. What would happen if one of the knights or bishops made a lot of moves or opened a lot of presents before the others? The other brothers and sisters would be unhappy. Therefore, you want to take turns, so all the children are happy.

Everyone likes to get lots of presents, but we also want good presents. The best presents are closer to the center of the board. Presents on the edge of the board or the rim are presents that you don't want to get - like socks!

Opening Presents Sample Game

1.e4 e5

Moving the babies to let the bishops develop and controlling the center.

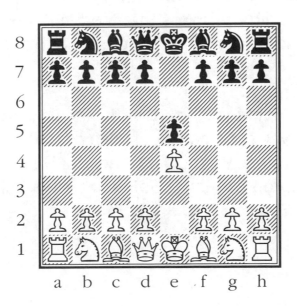

Now we want to develop (open a present with) the knight on g1. The choices are 2.Nh3, 2.Nf3, and 2.Ne2.

2.Nh3: Remember the old chess rhyme? "A knight on the rim is dim." The rim of the board is the outer edge. Because knights are slow-moving pieces, they want to be in the center of the board where most of the action is and they can get to any other part of the board quickly. A knight on h3 would have a long journey to get to the queenside.

2.Ne2: This attacks the d4 center square. But let's think of everyone's happiness. The bishop on f1 was happy when the baby (pawn) on e2 moved off his present. Now his brother, the knight, jumped onto his present and made him sad again. A good strategy is to avoid blocking the bishops, especially with pawns, so that they can develop toward the center.

2.Nf3: The best knight move because it develops toward the center, attacking d4 and the pawn on e5. 2.Nf3 also doesn't block the bishop on f1.

2.Nf3

Always remember to ask yourself after your opponent makes his move, "What is he threatening?" Figure out what your opponent is trying to do to you before you start thinking about what to do to him. Remember, his pieces are as important as yours. He is also trying to keep his family happy.

Black should notice that his pawn on e5 is attacked by White's knight. The pawn needs to be protected. Can this be achieved while opening a present with one of the young children? Yes, by either 2…Nc6 or 2…Bd6. Which move is better? The problem with 2…Bd6 is that the bishop blocks the d7 pawn (a center pawn), which also blocks in the bishop on c8. Black plays…

2…Nc6

White asks himself, "What is Black threatening?" Nothing, he is protecting the pawn on e5 and developing the knight. Okay, let's open a present with the bishop on f1. 3.Be2 is passive [holding back], 3.Bd3 blocks the d2 pawn, which blocks the bishop on c1, and 3.Ba6 leaves the bishop open to capture by Black's a6 pawn. 3.Bc4 or 3.Bb5 are both normal opening moves. For this example, White plays…

3.Bc4

3.Bc4 is a good move because it controls a center square (d5) and develops the bishop. What does it threaten? The f7 pawn is now attacked, but is also protected by the Black king. The bishop is worth 3 and pawn is worth 1, so taking the pawn on f7 would be a mistake for White even though it is a check and partially opens up the Black king because it gives up material (points). Let's say Black will now develop his f8 bishop. 3...Be7 is passive, 3...Bd6 blocks the d7 pawn, 3...Ba3 loses the bishop (to the pawn or knight), 3...Bb4 is okay, but 3...Bc5 looks like the best move since it also controls the d4 square (a center square).

3...Bc5

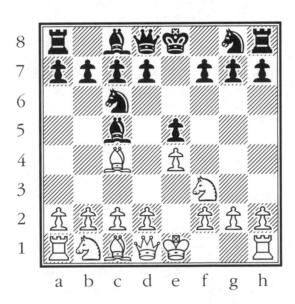

This attacks the f2 pawn, which is defended by the king. What should White play? Good moves are 4.Nc3 because it develops another piece, 4.d3 because it opens up the diagonal for the dark-squared bishop on c1, and 4.c3 since it threatens 5.d4, trying to control the center squares with pawns. Castling may be the best move because it is important to get the king out of the center of the board as soon as possible.

4.0-0

Castling has the double benefit of getting the king to safety and developing the rook. Remember the rook is a teenage brother or sister. When you castle, not only does your dad (the king) get a present, but the teenager also gets a present. What is the best present for a teenager? A CAR!! Why? Because it gives them freedom to go where they want. Castling gives rooks a car so they can speed towards the center.

Many years ago the children in one of my kindergarten classes suggested that if you don't castle, your teenagers get a worm! Of course, the car is a much better present than a worm.

It is normally best to castle as early in the game as you can. Most teenagers want to get a car when they are as young as possible.

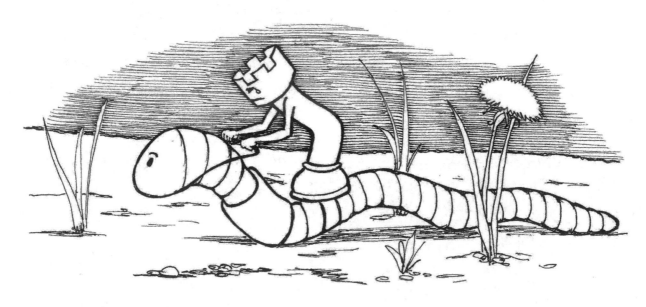

4...Nf6

This is a good move because it opens another present and prepares to castle or get Black's teenagers a car. Black threatens the pawn on e4. So White opens a present and defends the pawn at the same time by playing...

5.Nc3

Black can now get a car for his teenagers by playing...

5...0-0

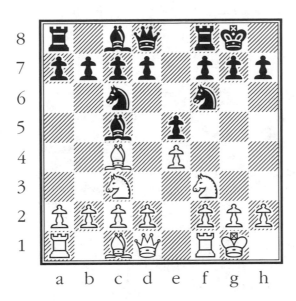

Notice that the position is symmetrical. All the Black pieces are on squares that are the mirror image of the ones the White pieces are on.

Which of White's young children hasn't opened his first present? The bishop on c1...but there is a baby on the present...so we must first move the baby. 6.d4 looks like a good move that controls the center, but the pawn would be attacked three times (pawn, knight, and bishop) and only defended twice (knight and queen). This would lose the pawn. So White plays...

6.d3

Say that Black continues to copy White and plays...

6...d6

White's best dark-squared bishop moves are 7.Bg5 or 7.Be3. Have White play....

7.Be3

Attacking the bishop on c5. Notice that the Black bishop is defended by the pawn on d6. Have Black play…

7…Bxe3

Capturing White's bishop. White's bishop gets grounded and his present is given to Black's children. So White grounds Black's bishop by playing…

8.fxe3

Now Black can have his last child open a present by playing…

8…Bg4

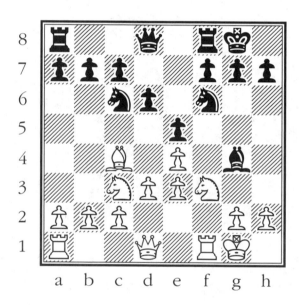

All the younger children have opened their first present and are happy. Now, after letting her children go first, White's mom can open her first present. Both 9.Qd2 and 9.Qe2 are fine here. Say White plays…

9.Qd2

Black's queen now opens her first present, so…

9…Qd7

The rooks work best when they are connected with each other and no other piece is between them. Rooks also like open files (a file not blocked by pawns) because they can move into the opponent's territory. When you are a teenager (rook), do you think you would rather hang out with adults (king and queen), babies (pawns), young children (knights and bishops), or other teenagers (rooks)? Other teenagers, of course! Rooks like to be together. Say the game continues...

10.Rad1 Rad8

Since both of the rooks can move to the d-file, you must designate which one moved when you record the score (See Scorekeeping, Lesson 3). In this case, both players moved the rook on the a-file.

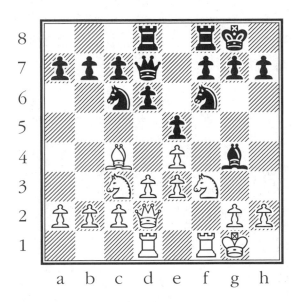

This completes the opening and we are headed into the middlegame. The opening goals are usually accomplished in the first ten moves or so of the game. Here we can say that White and Black both did a good job accomplishing their opening goals: control of the center; all the young children (knights and bishops) opened at least one present; and the teenagers (rooks) got cars (castled), not worms, and are hanging out together.

Notice that the queens (moms) didn't open their presents before the children and the pawns in front of both castled kings haven't moved and are providing protection for the kings. Also, equal-valued children got grounded (the dark-squared bishops).

Beating the Scholar's Mate

Some children have been exposed to the Scholar's Mate, or what some children call the "Four-Move Checkmate." The Scholar's Mate is not good chess because one side (usually White) brings the queen out early. He is trying to checkmate Black quickly on f7 with the aid of a bishop. This only works if Black doesn't see the threat (because he didn't ask himself, "What is White threatening?"). If Black sees the threat, the queen move is bad because she is in danger of being attacked and chased all over the board by the other player's knights and bishops.

It may look good at first to bring your queen out early, but you should ALWAYS assume the other player will make the best move.

Here is a typical Scholar's Mate pattern.

1.e4 e5 2.Bc4 Nc6 3.Qf3? (or 3.Qh5? g6 4.Qf3 Nf6)

Bringing out the queen early and threatening checkmate on f7.

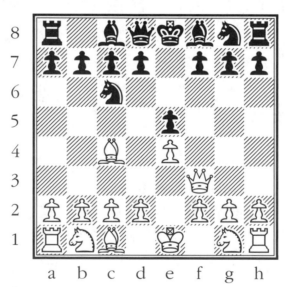

3...Bc5?? 4.Qxf7 mate.

If Black plays 3...Nf6 (instead of 3...Bc5??) and then 4...0-0, White wasted a queen move and placed her on a square where she soon may be chased away (by say ...Nc6-d4). Bringing out the queen early also prevents White's knight from developing to its natural f3 square.

Even though you may win some quick games by bringing the queen out early, it is recommended that you follow good chess principles and develop her later. After all, you will usually beat an opponent who doesn't ask himself what you are threatening, so follow good chess principles when you play.

Basset Hound Problems

 **2-1**

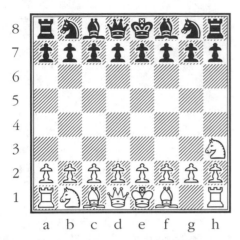

Was 1.Nh3 a good move for White? Why?

_____

 **2-2**

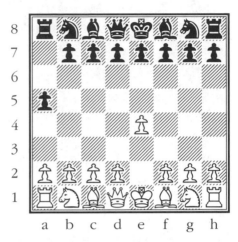

Was Black's pawn move 1…a5 a good move? Why?

_____

 **2-3**

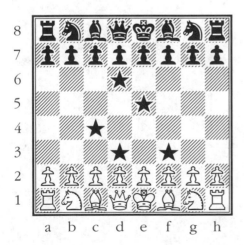

Which of the starred squares is the most important in the opening? Why?

_____

 **2-4**

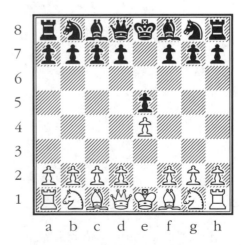

Is it better for White to move his bishop to d3, c4, or a6? Why?

_____

 **2-5**

 **2-6**

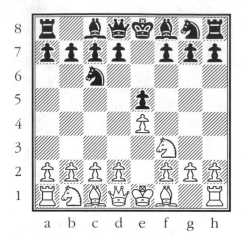

Is it a better move for White to move his pawn on d2 to d3 or d4? Why?

_____

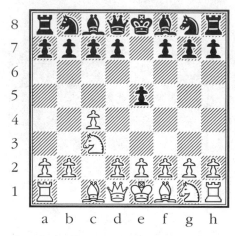

Black touches his knight on g8. Is it better to move it to h6, f6, or e7? Why?

_____

 **2-7**

 **2-8**

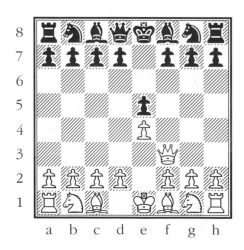

Is 2.Qf3 a good move? Why?

_____

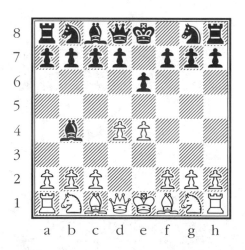

Black played 2…Bb4+. Which of these moves is best for White - 3.Ke2, 3.Qd2, or 3.c3? Why?

_____

 # 2-9

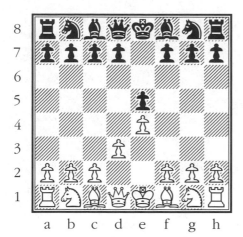

**White played 2.d3.
Is it a good move? Why?**

 # 2-10

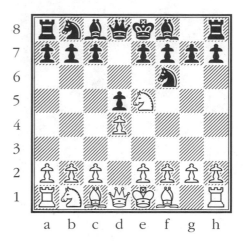

**White moved his knight from f3
to e5. Is this a good move? Why?**

Chess Detective Problems

 # 2-11

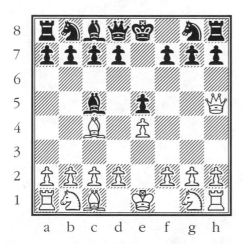

**White played 3.Qh5.
What is he threatening?**

 # 2-12

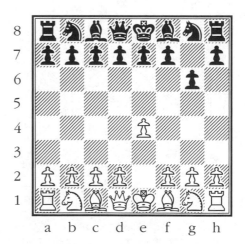

**Which of these is White's best move -
2.Bd3, 2.Bb5, 2.Be2, or 2.d4?**

 **2-13**

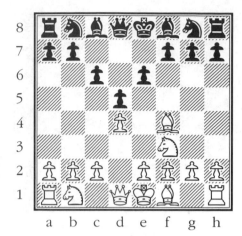

Which of Black's minor pieces will be the most difficult to develop to a good square?

_____

 **2-14**

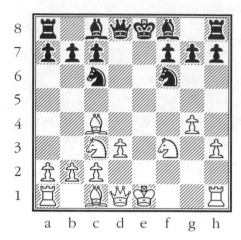

White wants to castle quickly. Is castling kingside a good idea?

_____

 2-15

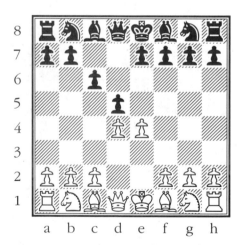

Which of these developing moves is best for White: 3.Nf3, 3.Qf3, 3.Nc3, or 3.Bf4? Why?

_____

 2-16

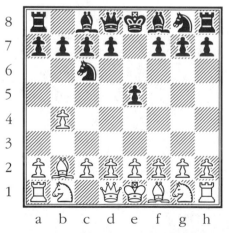

Black played 2...Nc6, protecting his e5 pawn from the bishop and developing a knight. Is this a good move? Why?

_____

2-17

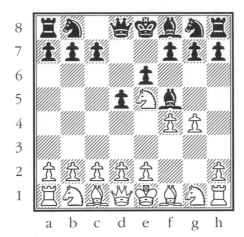

Black's last move was 4…e6.
White can take the bishop on f5 with
his g-pawn. Is this a good move?

2-18

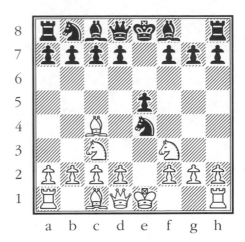

White played 4.Nc3. Which is
Black's best response – 4…Nxc3,
4…Nc5, 4…Bd6, or 4…d5? Why?

2-19

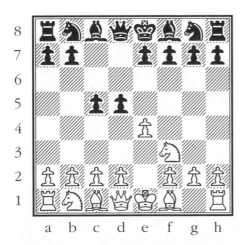

Black just played 2…d5 to try to control
the center. Is this a good move?

2-20

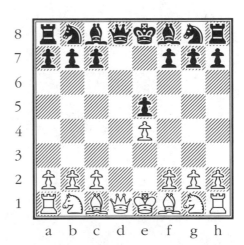

Is it a good move for White to capture
the Black queen with his queen?

LESSON 3

SCOREKEEPING

"...I have come to the personal conclusion that while all artists are not chess players, all chess players are artists."

Marcel Duchamp (1887-1968)
French artist

The language we read and write chess in is called algebraic notation. You can record the moves of a game in algebraic notation so that you can go back and play it over again later. Recording games is called scorekeeping.

Algebraic notation has two parts to it: the piece that moves and the square it moves to. A White move is written after the move number and a period. A Black move is written after the move number and three periods.

Remember the symbols for each piece – K is for king, Q for queen, R for rook, B for bishop, N for knight, and no letter or a blank is for the pawn.

On the first move of the game, say that White moves the pawn in front of his king two squares forward. This would be scored 1.e4.

Castling kingside is designated 0-0, and castling queenside is 0-0-0. The number of 0's is equal to the number of squares that the rook moves. Therefore, 0-0-0 for White would mean that the king moves from e1 to c1 and the queen's rook moves three squares from a1 to d1.

When a piece is captured, an x is placed between the piece making the capture and the square that the captured piece was resting on.

To show that a pawn has promoted, write the square the pawn promotes on, followed by an equal (=) sign, and the symbol for the promoted piece.

When a king is placed in check, a + sign is written after the move.

Sometimes a punctuation mark is placed after the move to explain how good or bad the move is.

!! is a brilliant move
! is a good move
!? is a move deserving attention
?! is a questionable move
? is a mistake
?? is a blunder

Here are some examples. Each example uses the diagram below:

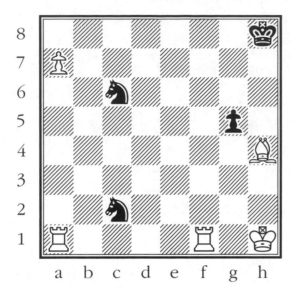

Pawn captures: Say it is Black's 32nd move and he captures the bishop with his g-pawn. It would be scored, 32…gxh4

Promoting a pawn: It is White's 45th move and he promotes the pawn to a queen, while putting the Black king in check. 45.a8=Q+ is how this move would be scored.

Two pieces of the same type can move to the same square: In this case the specific piece that is moving must be identified. It is preferred to identify the moving piece by the file (letter) instead of the rank (number), if possible.

Pretend that on White's 37th move and he moves his rook on a1 to c1. This move would be scored 37.Rac1 (as opposed to 37.Rfc1, which would be the case if the f1 rook moved to c1).

Let's say it is Black's 40th move and he moves the knight on c2 to d4. Since either knight can move to d4, the move should be written 40…N2d4. Note that 40…Ncd4 doesn't tell which knight moved, since they are both on the c-file.

Here is what a blank score sheet looks like. When you play a chess game, you want to fill it out as completely as possible. The space for Round is the game number and Board is the board number.

Event _____

Section _____ Round _____ Board _____ Date _____

White _____ Black _____

	White	Black		White	Black
1			31		
2			32		
3			33		
4			34		
5			35		
6			36		
7			37		
8			38		
9			39		
10			40		
11			41		
12			42		
13			43		
14			44		
15			45		
16			46		
17			47		
18			48		
19			49		
20			50		
21			51		
22			52		
23			53		
24			54		
25			55		
26			56		
27			57		
28			58		
29			59		
30			60		

circle result   **White Won**   **Draw**   **Black Won**

Signature   Signature

Here is one of the most famous chess games ever played. If they didn't keep score, we wouldn't be able to enjoy it today. The game took place at the Paris Opera House during the *Barber of Seville* opera in 1858. The great Paul Morphy of the United States played White against the Duke of Brunswick and Count Isouard.

Here are the moves of the game with a chess diagram showing each move.

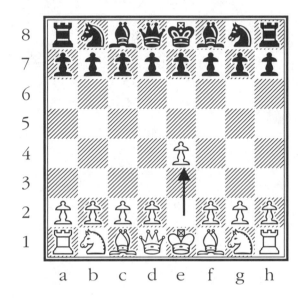

1.e4

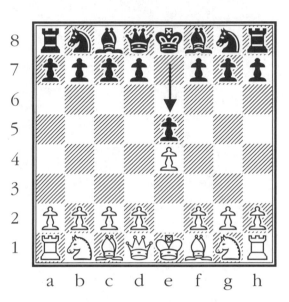

1...e5

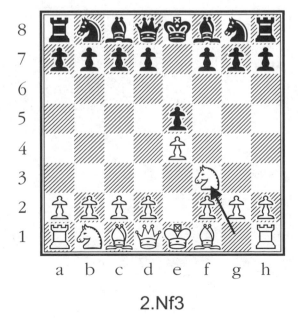

2.Nf3

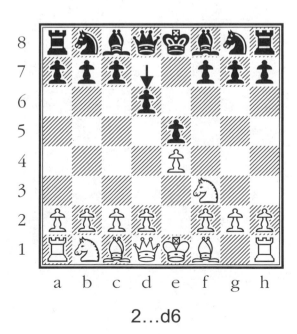

2...d6

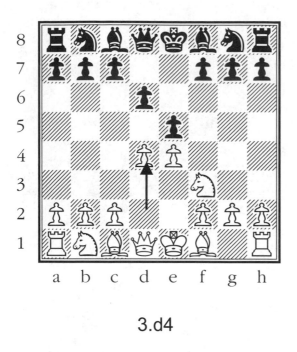

3.d4

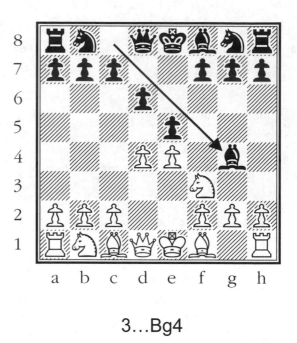

3...Bg4

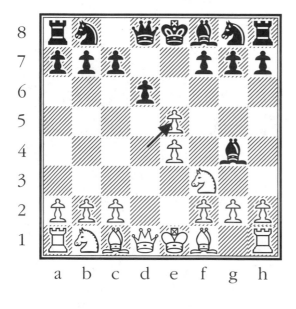

4.dxe5

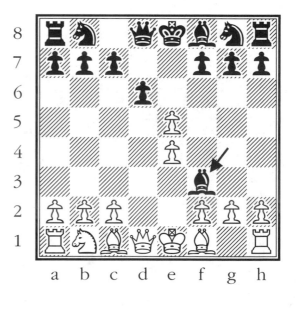

4...Bxf3

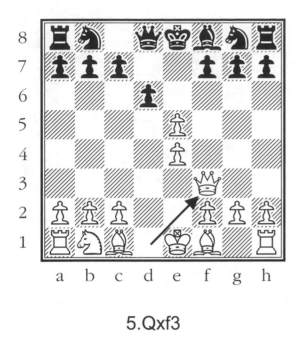

5.Qxf3

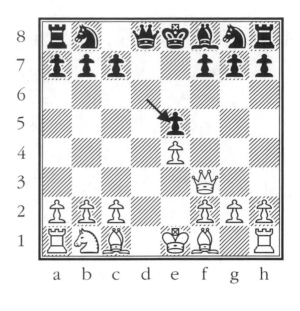

5…dxe5

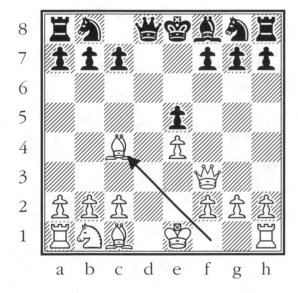

6.Bc4

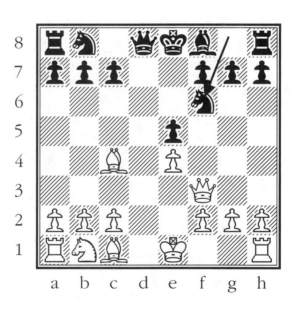

6…Nf6

7.Qb3

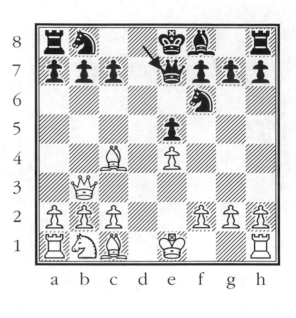

7...Qe7

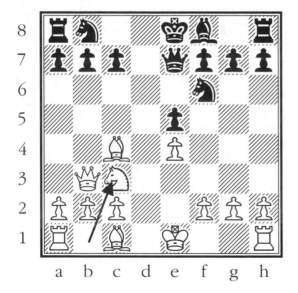

8.Nc3

8...c6

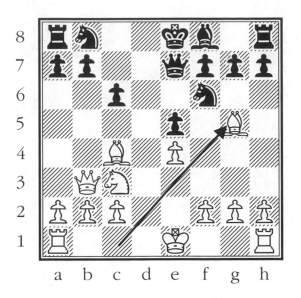

9.Bg5

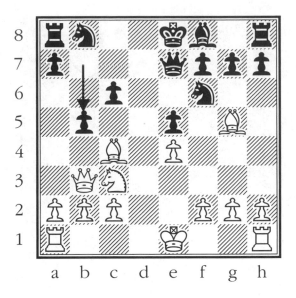

9…b5

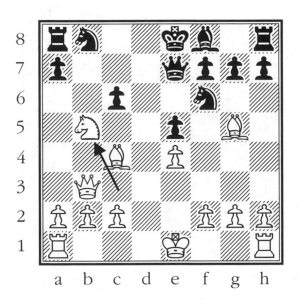

10.Nxb5!

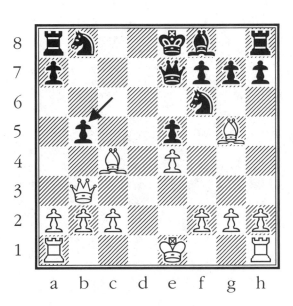

10…cxb5

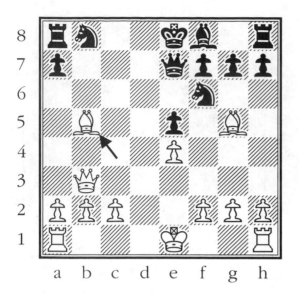

11.Bxb5+

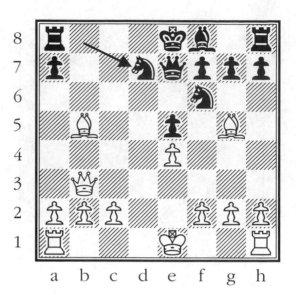

11...Nbd7

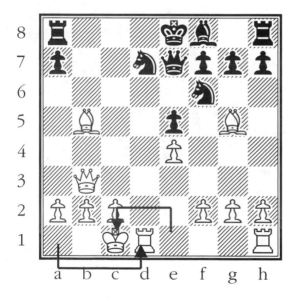

12.0-0-0

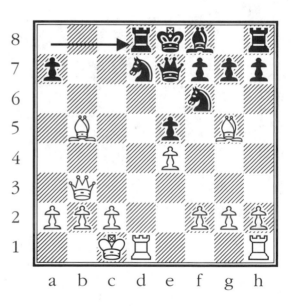

12...Rd8

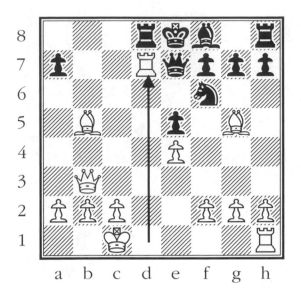

13.Rxd7!

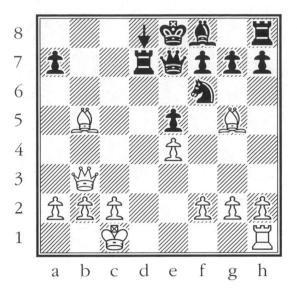

13…Rxd7

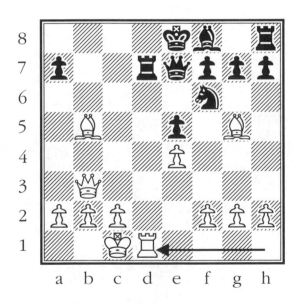

14.Rd1

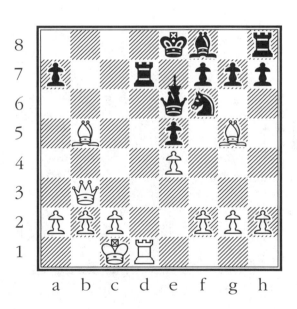

14…Qe6

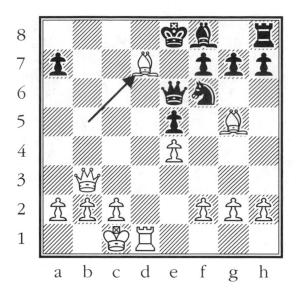

15.Bxd7+

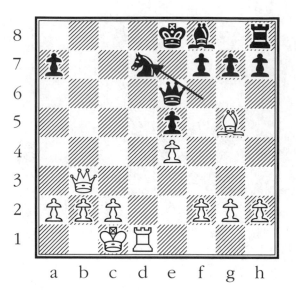

15…Nxd7

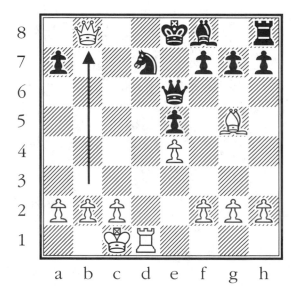

16.Qb8+!!

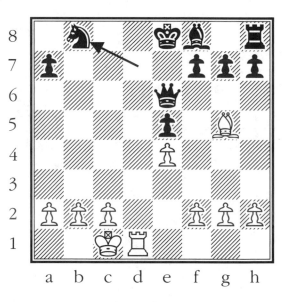

16…Nxb8

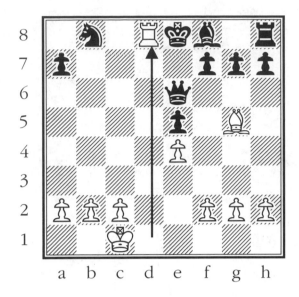

17.Rd8 mate (or checkmate)

Basset Hound Problems

Write the move shown by the arrow on the line below each problem. Include the proper move number and the number of periods after the move number. (Remember that there are three periods after the move number for a Black move.)

 3-1

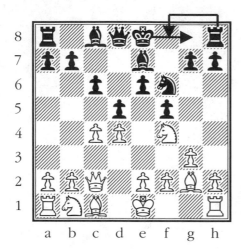

Black's 7th move

_____

 3-2

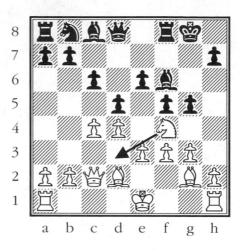

White's 12th move

_____

 3-3

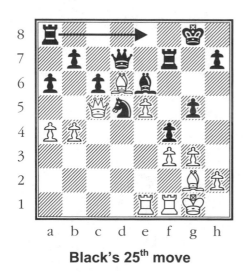

Black's 25th move

_____

 3-4

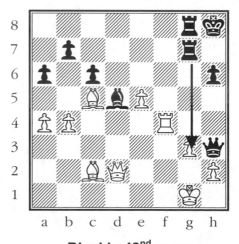

Black's 42nd move

_____

3-5

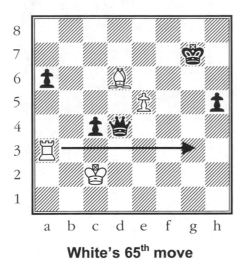

White's 65th move

_____

3-6

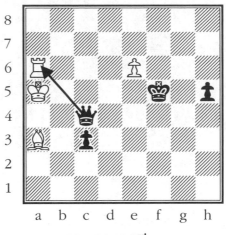

Black's 73rd move

_____

3-7

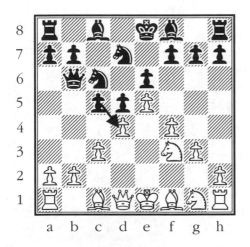

Black's 8th move

_____

3-8

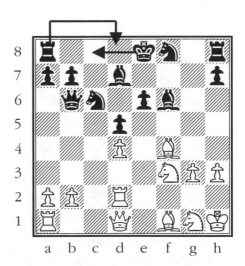

Black's 17th move

_____

3-9

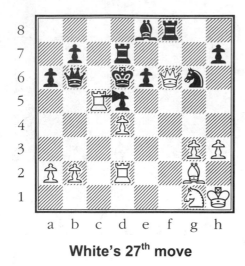

White's 27th move

_____

3-10

White's 39th move

_____

Chess Detective Problems

Write the move shown by the arrow on the line below each problem. Include the proper move number and the number of periods after the move number. These are trickier!

3-11

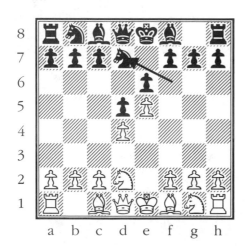

Black's 4th move

_____

3-12

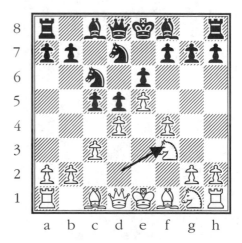

White's 7th move

_____

 **3-13**

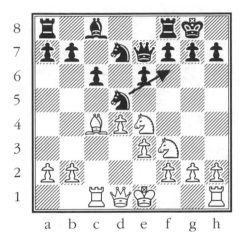

Black's 11ᵗʰ move

_____

 **3-14**

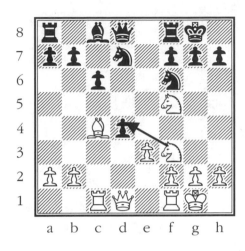

White's 15ᵗʰ move

_____

 3-15

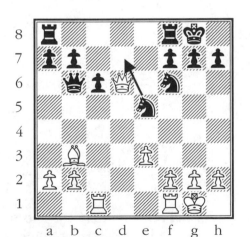

Black's 18ᵗʰ move

_____

3-16

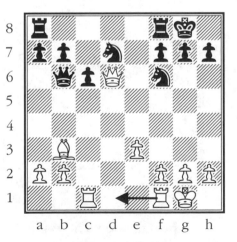

White's 19ᵗʰ move

_____

3-17

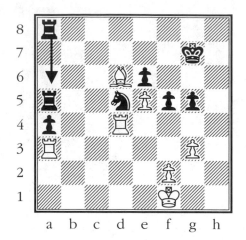

Black's 38th move

_____

3-18

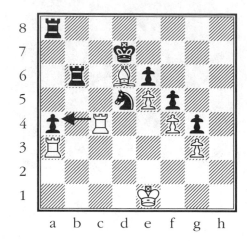

White's 48th move

_____

3-19

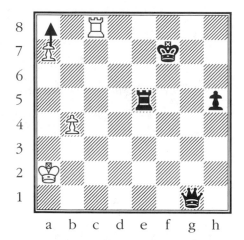

White's 51st move, promoting to a queen

_____

3-20

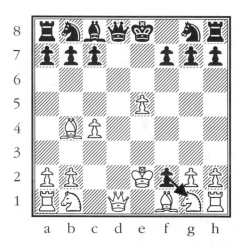

A Black pawn move that puts White in check (7th move)

_____

LESSON 4

BASIC CHECKMATES

"I play chess about four hours a day in training camp. You have to decide what move to use, or what combination of moves. I think less when I box because the reaction time is a lot quicker, but some people call me the chess boxer because they say I think too much in the ring."

Lennox Lewis
World Heavyweight Boxing Champion

The object of a chess game is to checkmate your opponent's king. This is achieved by attacking the king in a position where he cannot escape the check by moving (no available flight squares), capturing the checking piece, or interposing one of his own pieces in the line between the king and the attacker.

A position that can be similar to a checkmate is a stalemate.

By the rules of chess, when it is your turn to move, you must move. You are also not allowed to move your king into check where he can be captured.

Pretend that White's last move was Qf7 (from a7). Now Black must move. Black cannot move to g7 or h7 because the king would move into check from either the White queen or king. Black also cannot move to g8 because the queen attacks it. Since Black cannot move into check, he has no legal moves. Black has been stalemated by White and can claim a draw. *Draw* is a chess word for a tie.

Instead of playing Qf7, White could have played one of four moves that would have checkmated the Black king. What are they? Qa8, Qb8, Qg7, and Qh7.

Qa8 and Qb8 are checkmate because the queen attacks the king and controls the g8 square. The White king controls the g7 and h7 squares.

Qg7 and Qh7 are checkmate because the queen attacks the king and controls the g8 flight square while the White king protects the queen.

Remember that a stalemate is when you have no legal moves with ANY of your pieces, not just when the king has no legal moves.

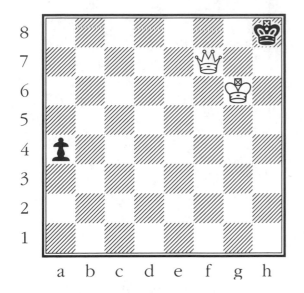

Consider this similar position where we add a Black pawn on a4. Unfortunately for Black, he now has a legal pawn move and he must play ...a3 and, in this case, cannot claim a stalemate.

The two kings can never be on squares next to each other where they touch. This would be illegal because one of the players would have put his king in check. Think of the kings as two magnets, with the positive poles facing each other. When the magnets get close to each other they repel each other, just like the two kings in chess.

Here are some examples of checkmates:

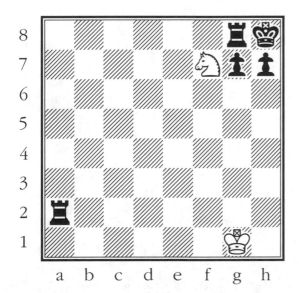

White's knight checkmates the Black king who is trapped by his rook and pawns.

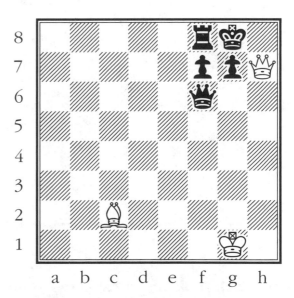

White's queen checkmates Black's king and controls the h8 square. The bishop defends the queen.

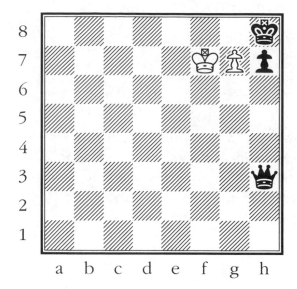

The White pawn checkmates the Black
king and is protected by the White king
who also prevents the escape to g8.

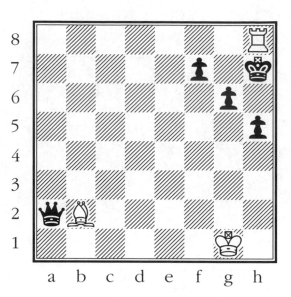

The White rook checkmates the Black
king and controls the g8 and h6 flight
squares. The White bishop protects
the rook and controls g7.

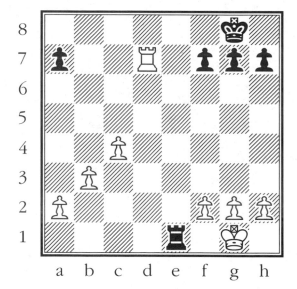

The Black rook checkmates the White
king and controls f1 and h1. This is called
a back rank checkmate because the king
is on the rank in back of the pawns.

The Black rook checkmates the White
king and prevents escape on a1 and a
a3. Black's knight controls the b1 and
b3 flight squares.

66

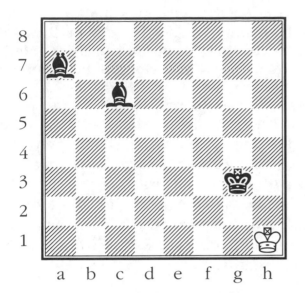

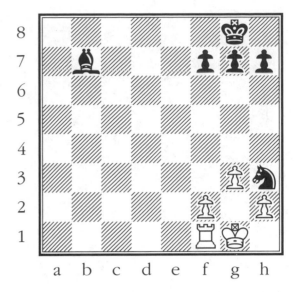

Black's light-squared bishop checkmates White's king. The dark-squared bishop controls g1 and the king attacks g2 and h2.

Black's knight checkmates White's king. The Black bishop controls g2 and h1.

Mating with a King and Queen vs. a King

The most basic checkmate to learn is the queen and king against a king. Often the queen is a promoted pawn.

In order to checkmate the king, he must be put in check and have all his flight squares taken away. On what part of the board is it easiest to checkmate the king…center, edge, or corner? Consider these positions.

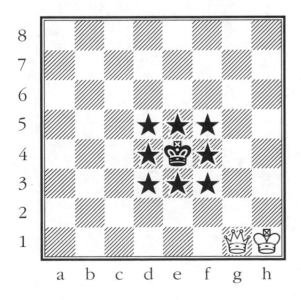

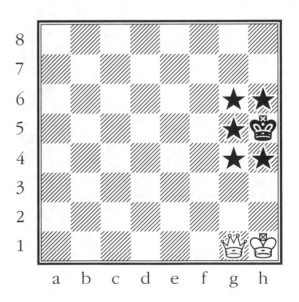

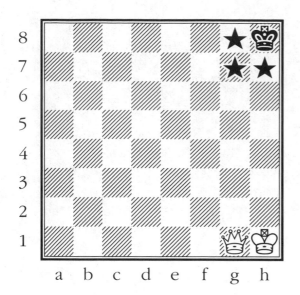

In order to checkmate the king in the first position (at the bottom of the last page with the Black king in the center), White must attack eight flight squares (marked by the stars) as well as e4, for a total of nine squares.

In the second position with the king on the edge of the board, White only has to eliminate five flight squares plus h5, for a total of six squares.

In the third position with the king in the corner, White only has to eliminate three flight squares plus h8, for a total of four squares.

It turns out the king can be checkmated both on the edge of the board or in a corner. Therefore, White's goal is to use his king and queen to force the Black king to one of these locations.

In order to do this, White uses his queen and king to form a "box" around the Black king. He then must shrink the box. It is important to make sure that you don't lose your queen and that the opposing king has a legal move when it is his turn up until the actual checkmate so that he will not be stalemated.

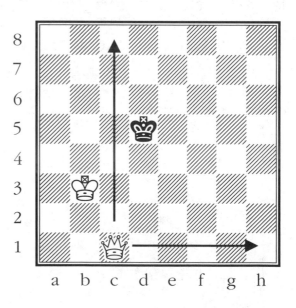

The "Box"

In the diagram at the bottom of the last page, the edges of the box (the way a queen moves) are marked with arrows. Notice that we are only defining the outer edges of the box, not the diagonals inside the box.

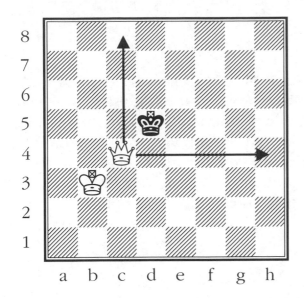

White shrinks the box by playing 1.Qc4+. Defining a different box, by playing 1.Qf4, is another possible solution. The goal is to checkmate the king as quickly as possible.

The Black king wants to stay near the center of the board, so he plays, **1...Ke5**. There are other possible solutions than the one given below. This solution will force the Black king toward the h8 corner. **2.Kc3 Kf5 3.Qd4** (shrinking the box) **3...Ke6 4.Kd3 Kf5 5.Qe4+ Kf6 6.Ke3 Kg5 7.Kf3 Kf6 8.Kf4 Kf7 9.Qe5 Kg6 10.Qf5+ Kg7 11.Qe6 Kf8** The goal is to first trap the opposing king against the edge of the board and then advance your king to help set up the checkmate. White continues, **12.Qd7 Kg8 13.Kg5 Kf8 14.Kg6 Kg8 15.Qd8 mate** (Note that 15.Qc8, 15.Qe8, and 15.Qg7 are all also checkmate).

A king and rook can also checkmate a lone king using the same procedure. While shrinking the box in this case, the king may have to protect the rook from the opposing king. The rook defines the box. The method for checkmating with a king and rook is the same as for a king and queen: shrink the box, trap the king against the edge of the board, and checkmate the king.

Queen and Rook Roller Mate

Here is another important basic mating pattern. If a player has a queen and a rook, his king is not needed to help force a checkmate since the queen and rook have the power to form a mating net on their own. Two queens or two rooks checkmate in a similar fashion. The idea is to shrink the box by alternating moves with the rook and queen.

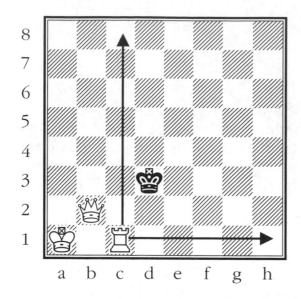

1.Rc3+ Kd4 2.Qb4+ Kd5 3.Rc5+ Kd6 4.Qb6+ Kd7 5.Rc7+ Kd8 6.Qb8 mate. Note that White could even blunder away the queen or rook and still have sufficient [enough] mating material to checkmate by shrinking the box and bringing in the king as shown on the last page.

You can think of shrinking the box like tossing a net over the king and pulling it tight to squeeze and capture him. A *mating net* is a chess term that describes when the king is under attack and checkmate cannot be avoided. The "net" controls the square the king is on and the flight squares around him to keep him from running away.

Back Rank Checkmate

A common type of checkmate, called a back rank mate, occurs when a king is attacked by a rook or queen on the first (or back) rank and is trapped by his own pawns on the second rank. A back rank checkmate is like a queen and rook roller mate, except that the king's pawns do the job of either the rook or queen that prevents the king's escape. A way to avoid a back rank checkmate is to keep your rooks on the first rank or to move up one of the pawns in front of the king to create a flight square.

Here is a memorable position against a girl I played against in my second chess tournament, when I was ten years old. I was White and it was my move.

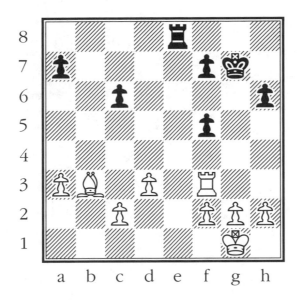

Things are looking good for our hero (me!) since White is safely ahead a bishop and a pawn. I couldn't resist the temptation to capture the pawn on f5 and played **32.Rxf5??**

She back rank mated me by playing **32...Re1 mate!** Remember it is always important to ask yourself what your opponent is threatening to do to you after each move!

Basset Hound Problems

 4-1

What queen move does the best job
of shrinking the box around the Black king?

_____

 4-2

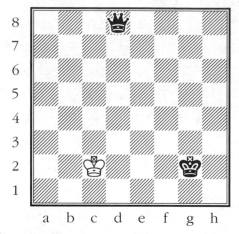

What queen move does the best job of
shrinking the box around the White king?

_____

 4-3

What rook move does the best job of
shrinking the box around the Black king?

_____

 4-4

What rook move does the best job of
shrinking the box around the White king?

_____

 **4-5**

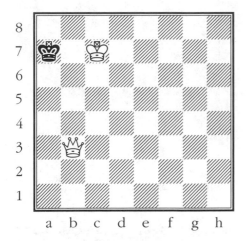

Which is a better queen move –
Qb8+ or Qb7+? Why?

 **4-6**

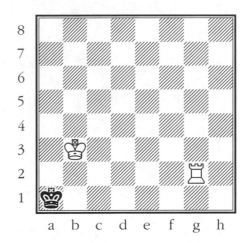

Which is the best rook move -
Ra2+, Rb2, or Rg1+? Which is the
worst of these moves? Why?

 **4-7**

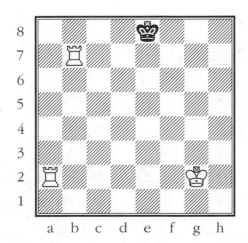

What is the best rook move for White?

 **4-8**

What is the best rook move for White?

4-9

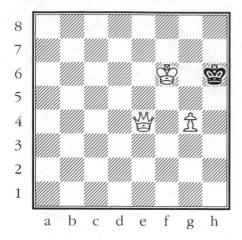

**What White moves checkmate the
Black king?**

_____ _____

4-10

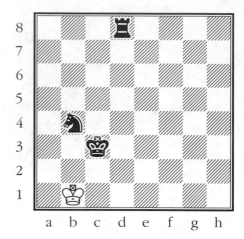

**What Black move checkmates the
White king?**

_____

Chess Detective Problems

4-11

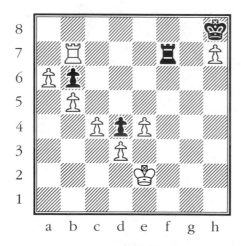

**White to move. Is 43.Rxf7 a good move?
Why?**

_____

4-12

What is Black's best move? Why?

_____

 4-13

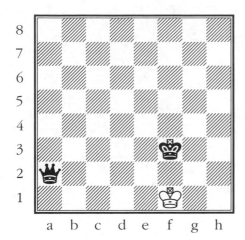

How many ways can Black checkmate
White on the next move?
What are the checkmate moves?

_____

 4-14

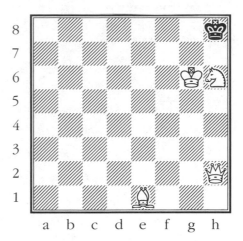

How many ways can White
checkmate Black on the next move?
What are the checkmate moves?

_____

4-15

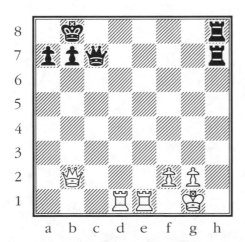

How many ways can Black checkmate
White on the next move?
What are the checkmate moves?

_____

4-16

How many ways can White
checkmate Black on the next move?
What are the checkmate moves?

_____

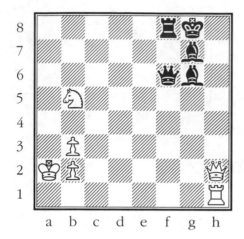

How many ways can Black checkmate
White on the next move?
What are the checkmate moves?

_____

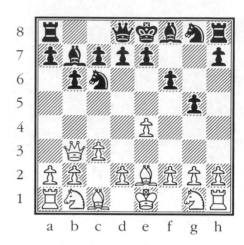

How many ways can White
checkmate Black on the next move?
What are the checkmate moves?

_____

 4-19

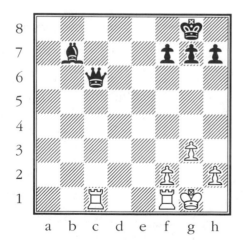

How many ways can Black checkmate
White on the next move?
What are the checkmate moves?

_____

 4-20

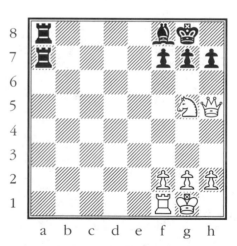

How many ways can White
checkmate Black on the next move?
What are the checkmate moves?

_____

LESSON 5

BASIC TACTICS

"The game of baseball between pitcher and hitter sets up like a game of chess in that you have to anticipate several moves or pitches ahead to set up your opponent."

Brad Lidge
All-Star Major League Baseball Pitcher

Tactics are battles between pieces and involve short-term, immediate threats and attacks. The different types of elementary tactics are:

- pin
- skewer
- fork
- discovered check
- discovered attack
- double check
- double attack

All of these tactics are different kinds of double threats. Sometimes it is difficult to defend two threats at once with only one move. Pins and forks are the most common types of tactics.

Combinations are a series of moves used to improve your position that include some or all of these tactical themes and can vary greatly in degrees of complexity.

In all of the examples in this chapter, the piece that performs the tactic can also do the same tactic from any of the starred squares.

Pin

A pin is when a long-range piece (queen, rook, or bishop) attacks a piece that shields another piece of greater value. If the pinned piece moves, the piece behind it would then be vulnerable to attack. It is a metaphor [a comparison] for a real pin: a thin, long, pointed piece of metal that can poke through different layers of clothing, in a straight line.

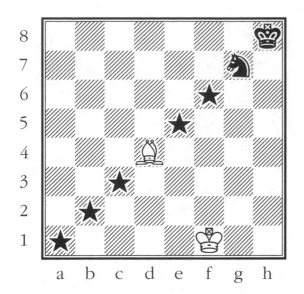

The White bishop pins the Black knight to the Black king. In this case, the less valuable piece, the knight, is in front of the more valuable piece, the king. In order for the knight to move again, the king must break the pin by first moving to g8 or h7.

When a piece is pinned to the king, it is called an "absolute pin" because the pinned piece absolutely cannot move, since the king would be placed in check.

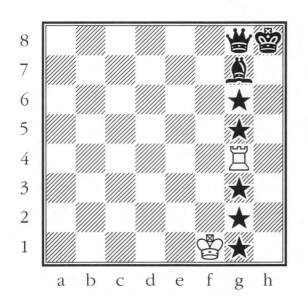

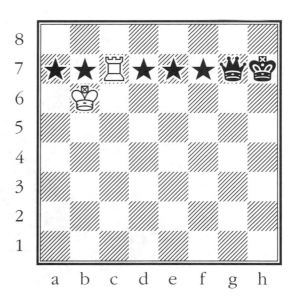

Examples of pins with a rook.

If the bishop moves, the rook will capture the queen. The bishop is pinned to the queen.

The rook will able to trade itself for the queen. The queen is in an absolute pin.

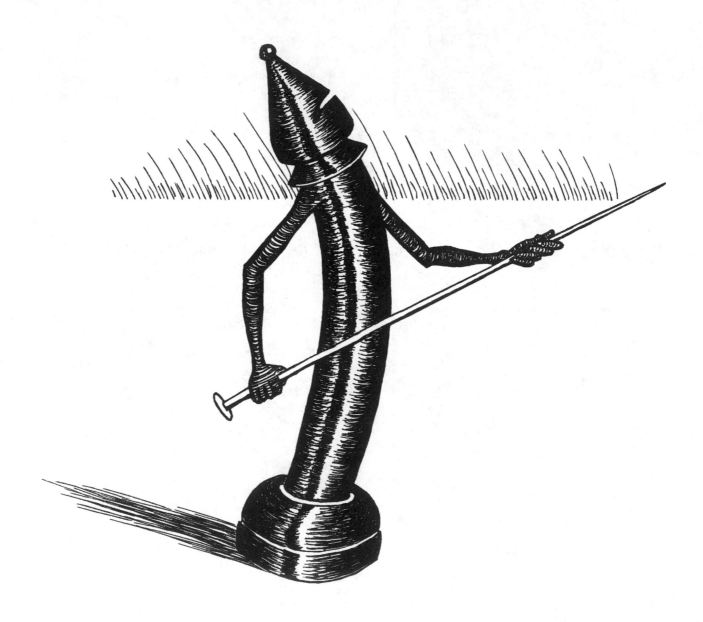

PIN

Since the queen has the powers of both the rook and the bishop, she can pin on ranks, files, and diagonals. Once again, a pin would occur if the queen were placed on any of the starred squares.

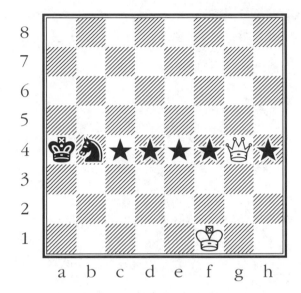

The White queen pins the knight to the king.

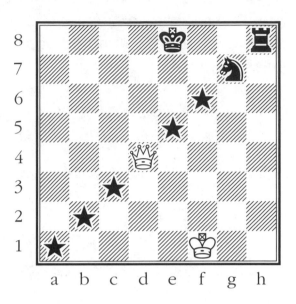

The White queen pins the knight to the rook.

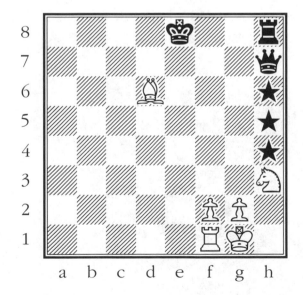

Here the White knight is pinned to the h1-square. If the White knight were to move, Black would play ...Qh1 mate.

Skewer

Skewers work the same way as pins, except now the more valuable piece is in front of the less valuable one. A skewer is the stick in a shish-ka-bob. Skewers, also known as x-rays, are less common than pins. The less valuable hidden piece usually ends up getting captured after the more valuable piece in front of it moves to safety.

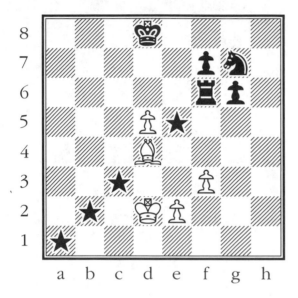
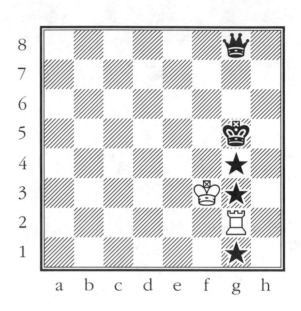

The bishop skewers the rook to the knight. If the rook moves, the bishop can capture the knight.

The rook skewers the king to the queen. When the king moves, the rook can capture the queen.

Fork

A fork is when a piece attacks two or more pieces. This is like at dinner when you are eating beans with a fork and the fork is used to stab two or more beans at once. Since the other player only gets one move, he has to choose which piece to save.

All the pieces have the potential to fork. Here are examples of each type of White piece forking two Black pieces. The starred squares represent other places where the White piece could also fork the Black pieces.

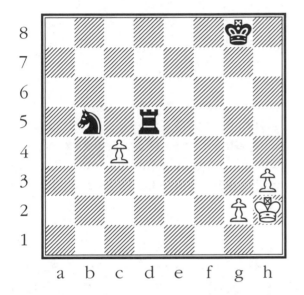

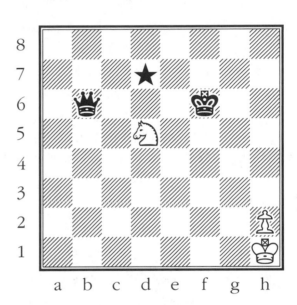

The pawn on c4 forks the knight and rook. Black should move the rook to save it and White's pawn can capture the knight.

The knight forks the king and queen. The king must move and then the knight can capture the queen.

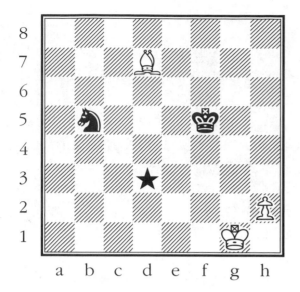

The bishop forks the king and knight.
The king must move and the bishop can
capture the knight.

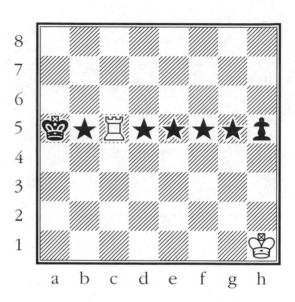

The rook forks the king and pawn.
The Black king must move and the
rook can capture the pawn. If the rook
was on b5, the king could capture it.

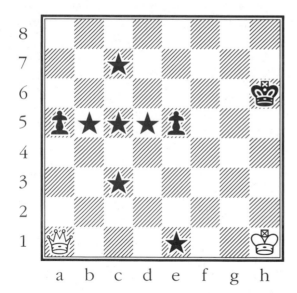

The queen forks the two pawns.
White can win one of the pawns on
the next move.

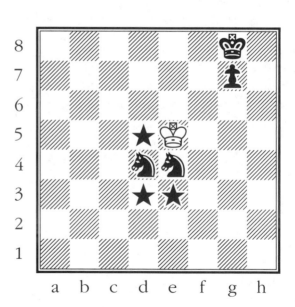

The king forks the two knights.
White can win one of the knights on
the next move.

Discovered Check

Discovered check occurs when a player moves a piece that shields the opposing king from check by one of the long-range pieces. It is kind of like playing peek-a-boo. When you move your hands from in front of your eyes, you can see the other person.

If the White knight moves, the rook will check the Black king.

Discovered Attack

A discovered attack is the same concept as a discovered check, except the attacked piece is not the king.

If White moves his bishop, he will make a discovered attack on the knight with the queen.

Double Check

Double check occurs when a piece moves to put the king in check while uncovering a long-range piece behind it that also attacks the king. A double check forces a king move because both of the attacking pieces cannot be captured or blocked in only one move.

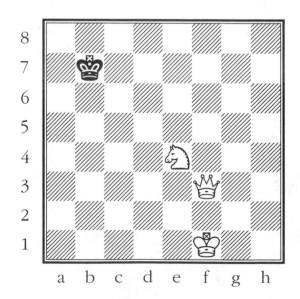

If White moved the knight to either c5 or d6, the Black king would be in double check from both the knight and the queen.

Double Attack

A double attack is the same concept as a double check, except that the attacked piece is not the king.

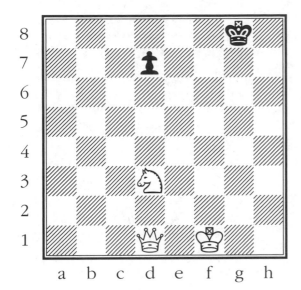

If White plays either Nc5 or Ne5, the Black pawn would be double attacked by both the knight and the queen.

87

Basset Hound Problems

 ## 5-1

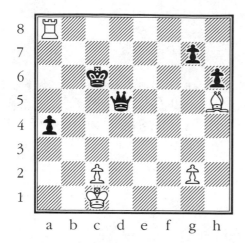

Find the pin for White that wins the Black queen

1._____

 ## 5-2

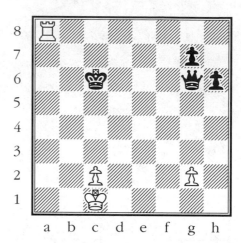

Find the skewer for White that wins the Black queen

1._____

 ## 5-3

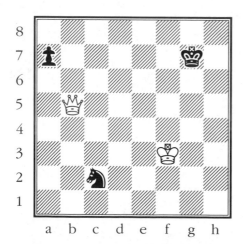

Find the move for Black that forks the king and queen

1..._____

 ## 5-4

Find the best skewer move for Black that wins the White queen

1..._____

5-5

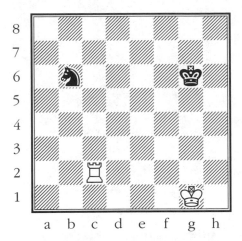

Find the move for White that forks the king and knight

1._____

5-6

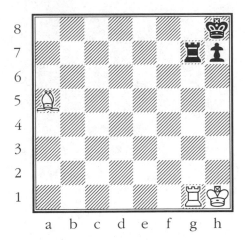

Find the move for White that pins the rook to the king

1._____

5-7

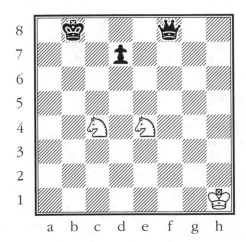

Find the moves for Black that fork White

1..._____ 1..._____ 1..._____

5-8

Find the skewer move for Black

1..._____

 5-9

**Find the move for White
that forks the king and queen**

1._____

 5-10

**Find the moves for White that
pin the bishop to the king**

1._____ 1._____

Chess Detective Problems

 5-11

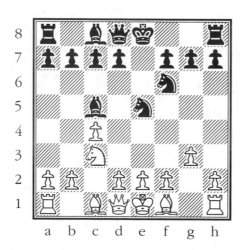

**Find the fork that wins back a piece
for a pawn for White.**

1._____

 5-12

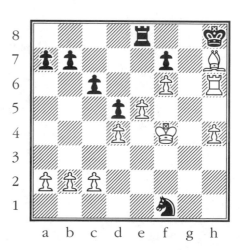

**Find the move that wins the
Black knight.**

1. _____

 5-13

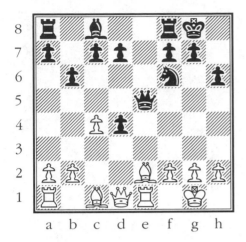

What move wins material for White?

1. _____

 5-14

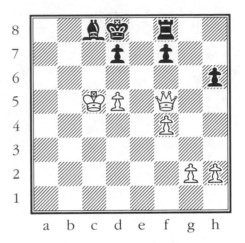

Black to move and win!

1... _____

 5-15

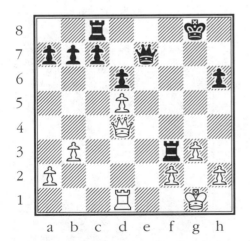

White is behind a rook for a pawn. What is his best move?

1. _____

 5-16

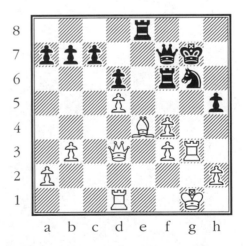

The Black knight is pinned to the king. What move should White play?

1. _____

 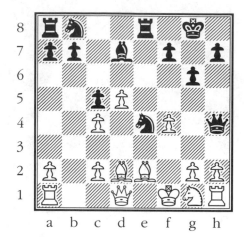

Black threatens ...Qf2 mate. What is White's only move that doesn't lose material or get checkmated?

1._____

 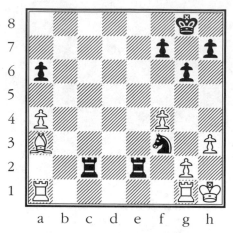

White can take the knight with his pawn. Is this a good idea? Why?

_____

 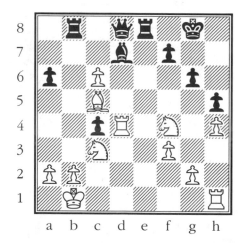

Black's bishop on d7 is pinned to the queen. How can Black save it?

1..._____

 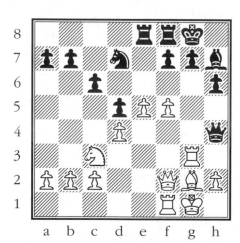

White to move and win the Black queen for a less valuable piece.

1._____

LESSON 6

DRAWS

"Chess is a good way to learn, to keep your brain fit and the ego in check, a mental form of your local gymnasium."

Abelard (1079-1142)
dialectician, philosopher, theologian

A chess game that ends in a tie is called a draw. Similar to sporting events that may end in a tie with a final score of zero to zero, or one to one, these types of draws can occur in chess:

- Insufficient mating material
- Stalemate
- Three-move repetition
- 50-move draw
- Draw by agreement (the draw offer)

Chess Clock draws:

- Both flags are down
- Flag is down, but player has insufficient mating material

In a chess tournament, the player who wins the game gets one point and the losing player gets zero points. Both players receive half a point for a draw.

Insufficient mating material

An insufficient [not enough] mating material draw occurs when neither player has enough material remaining on the board to force checkmate. An endgame where only the kings are left on the board would be an example of a draw by insufficient mating material. King + knight vs. king and king + bishop vs. king are also draws by insufficient mating material.

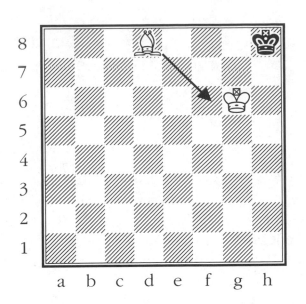

To show that a king and bishop are insufficient mating material, let's say that Black tried to lose by moving his king into the corner. The White king in this position is as close as he can get to the Black king and he controls both g7 and h7. If the white bishop is moved to f6, it puts the Black king in check. Notice that White cannot control the g8 flight square. Therefore, with only a bishop and a king, it impossible for White to checkmate Black and the game is drawn by insufficient mating material. A king and knight have similar problems mating a king.

Having one pawn remaining on the board is *not* insufficient mating material because the pawn has the potential to promote to a queen. A queen is sufficient mating material (see Lesson 4).

Stalemate

The rules of chess require that players must take turns moving. What if the player to move is not in check and has no legal moves available? This is called a stalemate and the game ends in a draw.

White is trying to win this position. Let's say White's last move was Rg7. Now it is Black's turn. What can he do? All the possible king moves (...Kg8, ...Kxg7, and ...Kh7) are illegal because he can't move into check. Since Black has no legal moves, the game is declared a draw by stalemate.

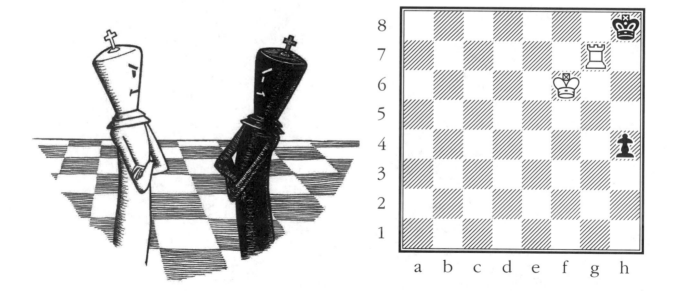

Here is the same position, but Black now has a pawn on h4. Unfortunately for Black, he cannot claim a stalemate if it is his move because he can move the pawn to h3.

Three-move repetition

If the same position (for both the White and Black pieces) occurs three different times, the game is drawn by three-move repetition. The moves do not have to repeat consecutively [one immediately following another], but usually do. The purpose of the three-move repetition draw is so the game doesn't repeat and go on forever.

The most common type of three-move repetition is perpetual [never ending] check. This occurs when one player, typically the one who is losing the game, finds a position where he can check the opposing king back and forth forever, with no way for the king to escape.

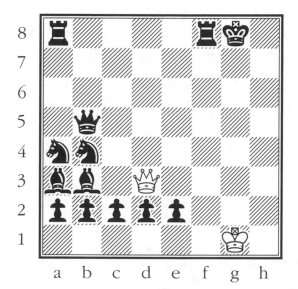

Black is way ahead in material and it looks like he is easily winning the game. Normally capturing the queen on b5 would be a good move, except that White needs a lot more material than a queen in order to have a chance.

But White can play 1.Qg6+. Black is then forced to play 1...Kh8. White can then continue 2.Qh6+ Kg8 3.Qg6+ (the second time for this position) 3...Kh8 4.Qh6+ Kg8 5.Qg6+ Now that the position has repeated the third time, White can claim a draw by three-move repetition.

Another way to look at a three-move repetition draw is to imagine that after every move, you take a photograph of the board. You then compare the photos. If three of the photos are identical with the same player to move, a three-move repetition draw can be claimed.

50-move draw

If fifty moves take place (a complete move is when both players have moved one time) and no pieces have been captured and no pawns have been moved, then the game is declared a draw. Fifty moves gives the player who is ahead a long time to figure out how to win; but the game cannot go on forever.

If a piece is captured or a pawn is moved, the fifty move count starts over again. A pawn move is progress toward promoting to a queen and a piece capture changes the position enough to justify starting over with the count.

The average length of a chess game between masters is about forty or fifty moves. The 50-move draw rarely occurs because the count to fifty moves usually starts after this point, late in the endgame. The 50-move draw would typically occur at the beginner level when the player with the advantage does not know how to checkmate the king.

Draw by agreement (the draw offer)

Either player can offer a draw. It is proper etiquette [manners] to offer a draw when you make your move, just before starting your opponent's clock. The draw offer stands for only one move. The opponent can accept the draw offer or decide to play on. If he chooses to continue the game, the draw offer goes away.

It is considered bad sportsmanship to continuously annoy your opponent by offering draws, which he has already refused (usually because he is ahead and is trying to win). Offering a draw on each move is like asking your mom for a cookie over and over again (and she keeps saying no)…she gets annoyed with you…usually pretty quickly! It is a better idea to wait a while and then say, "Mom, you look very pretty today. May I have a cookie?!"

Chess Clocks

A chess clock is two separate clocks in one housing, with a button above each clock. Only one clock runs at a time. When a player makes a move, he pushes the button above his clock, which stops his clock and starts his opponent's clock. It is proper chess etiquette to push the button with the same hand you used to move the piece.

Digital clocks are a newer invention and count down every second left in the game. Time runs out when the clock reads 0:00:00. Digital clocks have a time-delay feature that is useful in tournaments.

Analog clocks have a flag that is raised by the big hand a few minutes before the top of the hour. It is proper to set the clock so that the end of the time control is at 6:00. [For a 30 minute game (G/30), set the clocks at 5:30 at the start of the game. For a 60 minute game (G/60), set the clocks at 5:00.] At exactly 6:00 the flag will fall and the player will run out of time. In a tournament, only the players involved in the game are allowed to call the flag to claim a win on time. Even the tournament director cannot call the flag.

On this analog chess clock, the clock is running for the player on the left because the button on top of his clock is up. His flag is being lifted by the clock's big hand and in about two minutes, at 6:00, it will fall. The player on the right has about eight minutes left on his clock.

When the player on the left makes his move, he will push down his button, which will stop his clock and start the clock for the player on the right. The button above the clock of the player on the right will pop up when the left side button is pushed down.

In chess tournaments, you will be told how much time you have to make all of your moves in the game. In scholastic tournaments [tournaments for children], the time control is normally a game in 30 minutes for each player or a total game time of an hour. If a player runs out of time, his opponent can claim a win, provided he has sufficient mating material on the board.

You can use as much or as little time on each move as you like, but don't run out! It is best to pace yourself. If you move too fast, chances are you will make a mistake. If you move too slowly, the quality of your moves usually goes up, but you may run out of time and lose the game that way.

Using a clock in a chess game is like taking a test in school. If you spend all your time on the first problem, you may get it right, but you will do poorly on the test because you didn't answer the other questions. If you answer each question too quickly, the answers are usually wrong and incomplete. As both a student and a chess player, you must learn to find a balance.

Both flags are down

When both player's flags have fallen, they are both out of time. This is another type of draw, as long as one of the players notices that time has run out. Usually this occurs when both players are short of time, with their attention focused on the board when the first player runs out of time.

Flag is down, but player has insufficient mating material

If the player who claims a win on time has insufficient mating material, he can only claim a draw because a win is impossible on the board. All he needs is a pawn (the possibility to win) to claim a win on time because a pawn *can* promote to a queen, which is mating material.

Basset Hound Problems

 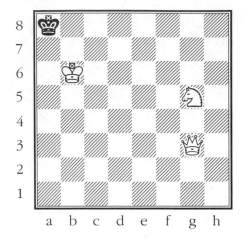

6-1

Which is the best move for White:
1.Qe3, 1.Qd6, or 1.Qb8+? Why?

_____

 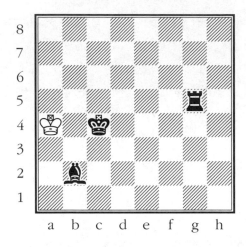

6-2

Which is the best move for Black:
1…Kc3, 1…Bc3, or 1...Rb5? Why?

_____

 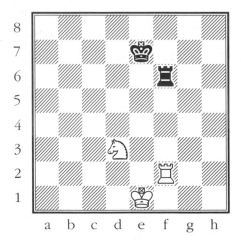

6-3

Which is the best move for Black:
1…Re6+, 1…Ra6, or 1…Rxf2? Why?

_____

6-4

Which is the best move for White:
1.Nb5+, 1.Nxc6, or 1.Nxe6? Why?

_____

 **6-5**

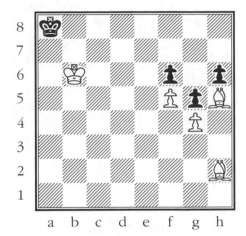

Which of these moves is the best move
for White: 1.Be8, 1.Bd6, or 1.Ka6? Why?

 **6-6**

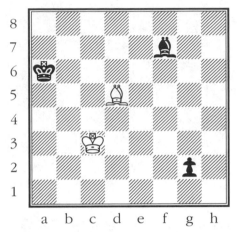

Which is the best move for White:
1.Bc4+, 1.Bxg2, or 1.Bxf7? Why?

 **6-7**

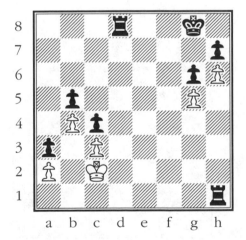

Which of these moves is the best move
for Black: 1...Rh2+, 1...Ra1, or 1...Rd5? Why?

 **6-8**

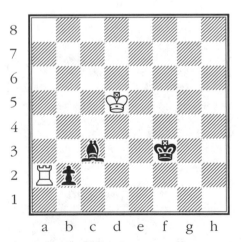

Which is the best move for White:
1.Rxb2, 1.Ra3, or 1.Kc4? Why?

 **6-9**

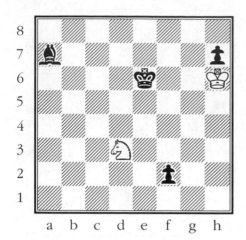

Which is the best move for White: 1.Nf5+, 1.Nxf2, or 1.Kxh7? Why?

 **6-10**

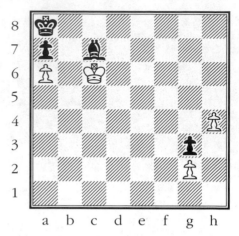

Which is the best move for White: 1.h5 or 1.Kxc7? Why?

Chess Detective Problems

 **6-11**

What is Black's best move?

1..._____

 **6-12**

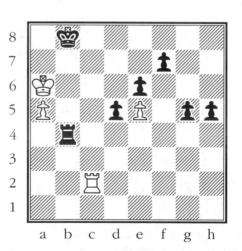

What is White's best move?

1._____

6-13

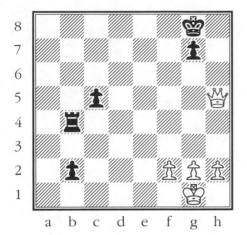

What is White's best move?

1._____

6-14

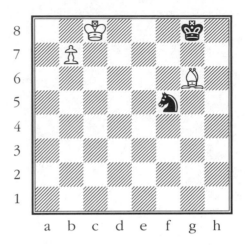

What is Black's best move?

1..._____

6-15

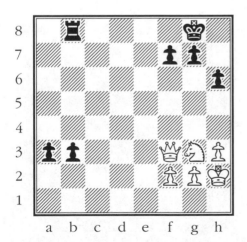

White is ahead in material. He played Kh2 and offered Black a draw. Should Black accept it? Why?

_____

6-16

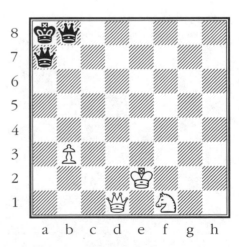

What is White's best move?

1._____

6-17

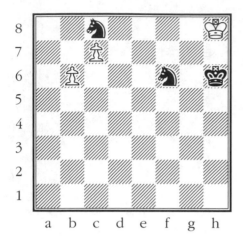

What is Black's best move?

1..._____

6-18

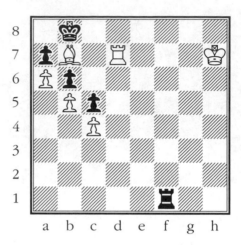

What is Black's best move?

1... _____

6-19

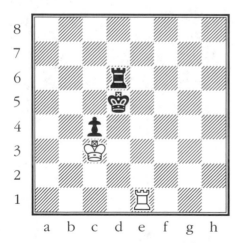

What is White's best move?

1._____

6-20

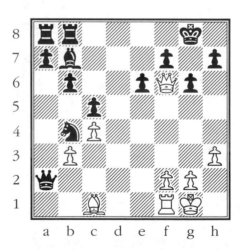

Black played ...Qxa2 and offered a draw. Should White accept it?

_____

LESSON 7

FREE STUFF!

"You must not, when you have gained a victory, use any triumphing or insulting expressions, nor show too much of the pleasure you feel; …"

Benjamin Franklin (1706-1790)
statesman, philosopher, inventor, scientist, musician, economist

The biggest mistake made by young chess players is hanging (leaving a piece open to capture, or in chess terms, *en prise*) their pieces. Of course, you should also look for pieces that your opponent hasn't protected. Most young players are only involved in their own plans and don't spend any time considering what their opponent is threatening. Always look to see what your opponent can do to you. In chess, remember that your opponent's pieces are as important as your own.

Counting the number of times a piece is attacked and defended is one of the most important concepts in chess. The most common form of "free stuff" at the beginner level is a piece that is attacked once and has no defender, making it possible to be captured the next move.

The reason why you don't leave your toys in the park is that some other kid may come, take them, and claim them as "free stuff." Try not to leave "free stuff" lying around on the chessboard. What do you do before you cross the street? Look both ways so that you don't get run over by a car. In chess, double-check your move so that you don't get run over by an opponent's piece! In other words, look before you leap!

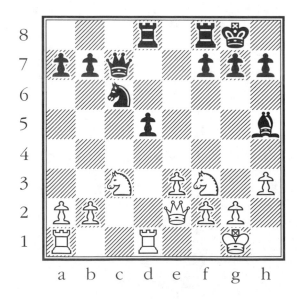

It is White to move. Notice that the Black pawn on d5 is attacked twice (by the knight on c3 and the rook on d1). It is only defended once (by the rook on d8). Because White has an extra attacker, he can safely capture the pawn with either the knight or the rook and win material. Think of it like two-on-one drills that you may have practiced in soccer. The two White pieces overpower the Black pawn.

In a similar position, remove Black's bishop from h5 and place it on e6. Now Black has two defenders for the d5 pawn. White still has two attackers. White would now lose material if he tried to capture the pawn. If White plays 1.Nxd5 Rxd5 2.Rxd5 Bxd5, he would then lose a knight and a rook for a pawn and a rook (a loss of two points). If Black responds 1...Bxd5 2.Rxd5 Rxd5, Black then wins a knight and rook for a bishop and pawn (a gain of 4 pawns).

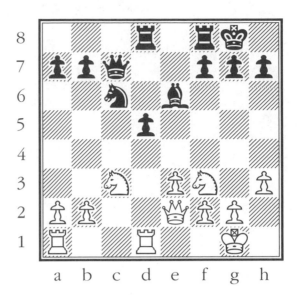

It is usually best to make a capture with your least valuable piece first so that you have the most material remaining at the end of the captures.

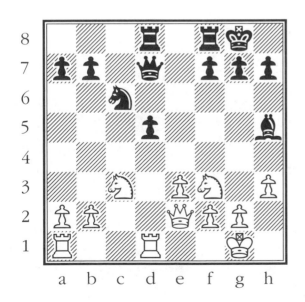

Now put the bishop back on h5 and place the Black queen on d7 instead of c7. Again the Black pawn is defended twice, this time by the queen on d7 and the rook on d8. Even though the pawn is only attacked twice, White can safely capture the pawn with either the knight or the rook because Black would have to re-capture with the queen first. The capture sequence could go 1.Rxd5 Qxd5 2.Nxd5 Rxd5. Black does end up with the last piece standing on d5, but he gave up a queen and a pawn (10) for a knight and a rook (8).

Sample Game Looking for "Free Stuff"

Set up your chessboard so that you can play along. Some of the moves in this game are bad because they leave "free stuff" for the opponent.

1.e4 b5?

The b5 pawn is hanging.

2.Bxb5 a6 3.Nf3?

The bishop is hanging.

3...axb5 4.d4 e6 5.Qe2 Ba6

Protecting the pawn.

6.h3 Nf6

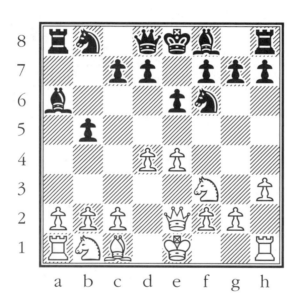

7.Qxb5?

The queen is now hanging, White forgot that Black defended the pawn when he played 5...Ba6.

7...Bxb5 8.Bg5 Nxe4?

The pawn is hanging...but the knight is pinned to the queen...oops!

9.Bxd8 Kxd8

It is important to recapture the bishop, so that at least Black gets something back for the queen. This is like getting change back after buying something at a store.

10.Nc3 Ba6?

Black noticed that the bishop is under attack, but the knight is too! Better moves that won't lose a piece are 10…Nxc3, 10…Nd6, 10…Bc6, or 10…Bb4.

11.Nxe4 Be7 12.0-0-0 Bb7

Attacking the knight on e4 with bishop and making a discovered attack on the a2 pawn by the rook. How can White defend them both?

12.Nc3!

12.Nc5? attacks the bishop on b7. Black can then win free stuff by playing 12…Bxc5 13.dxc5 Rxa2.

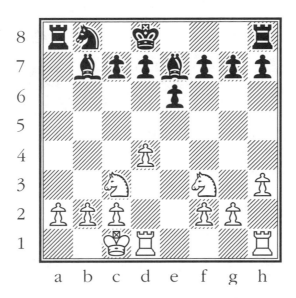

12…Bg5+?

Giving away the bishop. Remember you don't win the game by putting your opponent in check. Make sure each move has a purpose.

13.Nxg5

Taking the free bishop.

Basset Hound Problems

 7-1

White to move. Where is the free stuff?

_____

 7-2

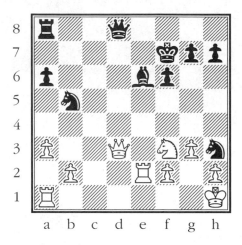

White to move. Where is the free stuff?

_____

 7-3

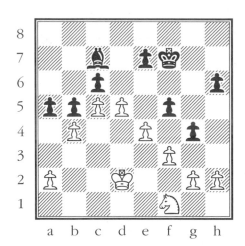

Black to move. Where is the free stuff?

_____

 7-4

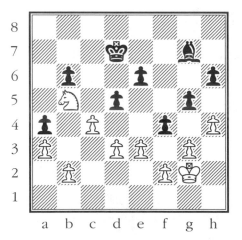

Black to move. Where is the free stuff?

_____

 **7-5**

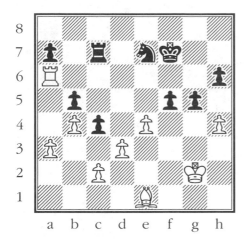

White to move. Where is the free stuff?

_____

 **7-6**

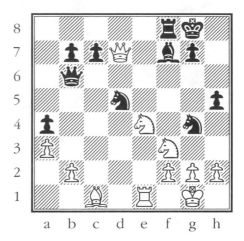

White to move. Where is the free stuff?

_____

 **7-7**

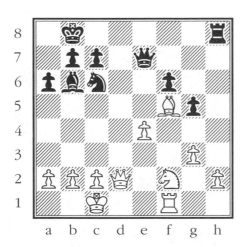

Black to move. Where is the free stuff?

_____

 **7-8**

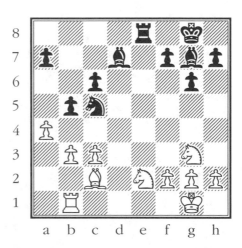

Black to move. Where is the free stuff?

_____

 7-9

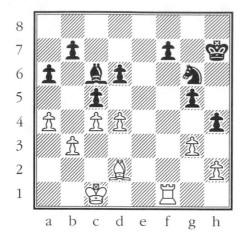

White to move. Where is the free stuff?

_____

 7-10

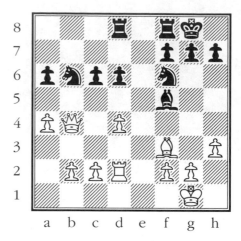

White to move. Where is the free stuff?

_____

Chess Detective Problems

 7-11

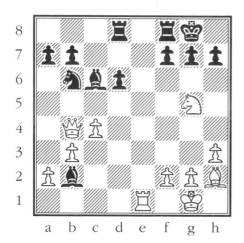

White to move. Where is the free stuff?

_____

 7-12

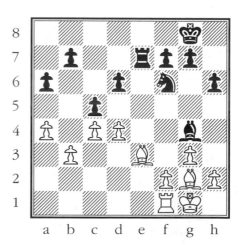

White to move. Where is the free stuff?

_____

 # 7-13

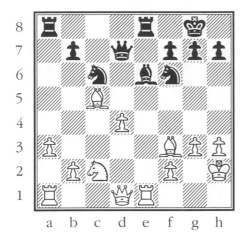

Black to move. Where is the free stuff?

_____

 # 7-14

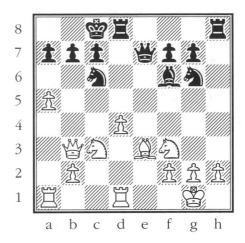

Black to move. Where is the free stuff?

_____

 # 7-15

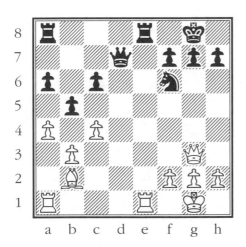

White to move. Where is the free stuff?

_____

 # 7-16

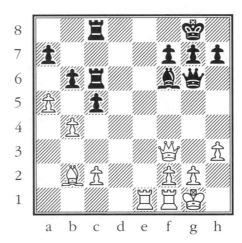

White to move. Where is the free stuff?

_____

 **7-17**

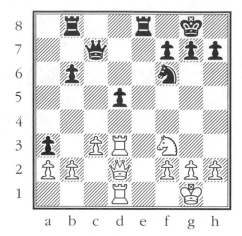

White to move. Where is the free stuff?

_____

 **7-18**

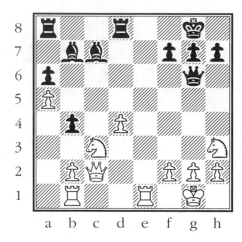

Black to move. Where is the free stuff?

_____

 7-19

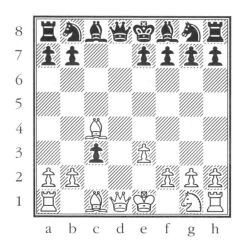

**White to move.
How do you win free stuff?**

_____

 **7-20**

**White to move.
How do you win free stuff?**

_____

LESSON 8

PAWN STRUCTURE

"But the enemy has the move, and he is about to open his full game. And pawns are as likely to see as much of it as any. Sharpen your blade!"

J. R. R. Tolkien (1892-1973)
Oxford professor, author of The Lord of the Rings

Pawn structure is an important element in chess. Pawns can be strong or weak depending on their position in relationship to the other pawns on the board. Since pawns must capture an opposing piece to change files (which usually requires the opponent's help) and change their structure, strong or weak pawns may last for the entire game.

Each player is trying to create a strong pawn structure for himself while, at the same time, trying to weaken his opponent's structure.

Don't help out your opponent's pawn structure. Think of the story of the Three Little Pigs. The big, bad, wolf didn't go to the little pig that was making his house out of straw and say, "You silly little pig. Straw doesn't make a strong structure. I ordered you some bricks to build your house out of, so that when I huff and puff, I won't be able to blow your house down!"

Pawns are stronger if they are side-by-side because they can protect each other. Weak pawns are typically lined up in front of one another on the same file, unable to provide protection for each other. It is good to have friends to protect you.

In master-level chess, losing a pawn because it is weak can be the difference between winning and losing the game.

Here are the different types of pawns:
- passed pawns
- protected passed pawns
- isolated pawns
- doubled isolated pawns
- tripled isolated pawns
- isolated passed pawns
- base pawns
- backward pawns
- doubled pawns
- tripled pawns

Passed Pawns

A passed pawn is a pawn that can move to the other side of the board and promote without an opponent's pawn blocking it or guarding squares in its path. Passed pawns are strong pawns because one of the opponent's pieces must guard against the pawn's attempt to promote to a queen. Rather than allowing the pawn to promote, often the defending player must give up a piece, say a bishop or knight, for the passed pawn. The further up the board a passed pawn is, the more dangerous it becomes.

The pawns on a5 and d3 are passed pawns.

Protected Passed Pawns

A protected passed pawn is a passed pawn that is protected by a friendly pawn. Protected passed pawns are the strongest pawns.

The pawn on e5 is a protected passed pawn. The pawn on f4 protects it.

Isolated Pawns

Isolated pawns are sad or weak pawns that are all alone because they have no other friendly pawns on adjacent [next to] files. Isolated pawns can be especially weak if they are on a half-open file (a file where one player has a pawn and the other player doesn't have a pawn) because the opposing rooks can line up and attack them.

Doubled Isolated Pawns

Doubled isolated pawns are two pawns lined up on the same file with no friendly pawn on an adjacent file to provide protection.

Tripled Isolated Pawns

Tripled isolated pawns are three pawns lined up on the same file with no friendly pawn on an adjacent file to provide protection. Tripled isolated pawns are somewhat rare.

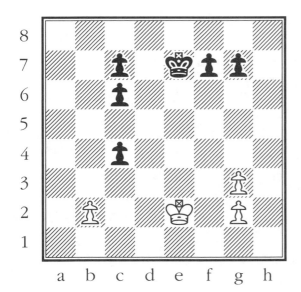

The pawn on b2 is an isolated pawn. The pawns on g2 and g3 are doubled isolated pawns and the pawns on c7, c6, and c4 are tripled isolated pawns.

Isolated Passed Pawns

An isolated passed pawn has the good trait of being passed and the bad trait of being isolated.

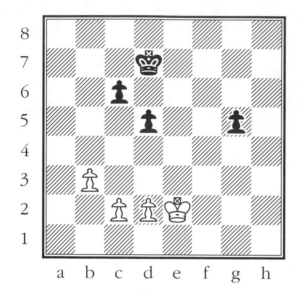

The g5 pawn is an isolated passed pawn.

Base Pawns

A base pawn is the pawn that is at the base of a pawn chain (pawns lined up diagonally on files next to each other) and has no pawn to protect it.

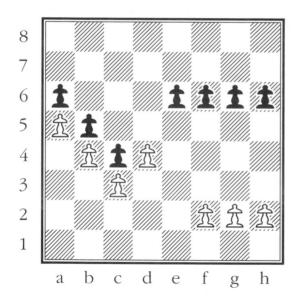

The pawns on a6 and c3 are base pawns.

Backward Pawns

A backward pawn is a base pawn on an opponent's half-open file. Often a backward pawn is weak because it can be easily attacked by the opponent's rooks on the half-open file.

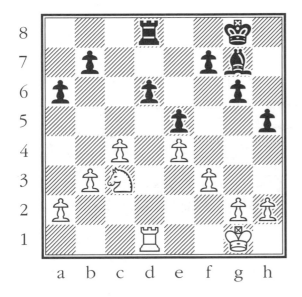

The pawns on a2, g2, b7, and f7 are base pawns. The pawn on d6 is a backward pawn.

Doubled Pawns

Doubled pawns are two pawns on the same file that have a pawn on an adjacent file that could provide protection. Doubled pawns are much stronger than doubled isolated pawns, but usually not as strong as having the pawns side-by-side.

Tripled Pawns

Tripled pawns are three pawns on the same file that have a pawn on an adjacent file that could protect them. Tripled pawns are fairly rare.

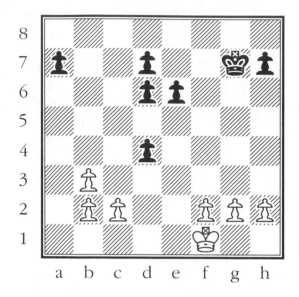

White's b-pawns are doubled pawns.

Black's d-pawns are tripled pawns.

Adding other pieces to the board has no effect on how pawns are defined.

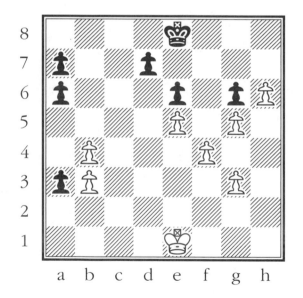

The h6 pawn is a protected passed pawn.

The a3 pawn is an isolated passed pawn.

The g6 pawn is an isolated pawn.

The base pawns are on g3 and d7.

The pawns on a3, a6, and a7 are tripled isolated pawns.

The b3 and b4 pawns are doubled isolated pawns.

The d7 pawn is a backward pawn because it is on a half-open file for White.

The g3 and g5 pawns are doubled pawns (not doubled isolated pawns because of the f4 and h6 pawns).

124

Playing for Pawn Structure advantages

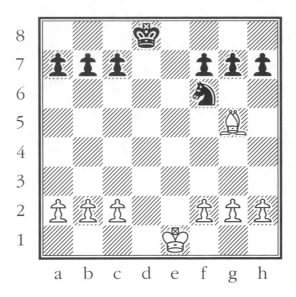

From a pawn structure point of view, what is White's best move in this position? **1.Bxf6+**, exchanging the bishop for the knight. Because Black does not want to end up behind a piece, he must recapture with **1...gxf6**. Now the pawn on h7 is isolated and the pawns on f7 and f6 are doubled isolated pawns. In one move, White was able to wreck Black's entire kingside pawn structure, making these pawns harder to defend later on in the game.

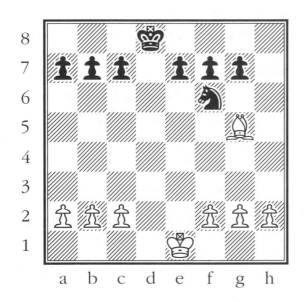

In this position, lets say White plays 1.Bxf6. Black needs to recapture the bishop with either 1...exf6 or 1...gxf6. Which is better? In either case Black will have doubled f-pawns. 1...exf6 is the correct move because if Black plays 1...gxf6, White's h2 pawn would become a passed pawn. With 1...exf6, the h2 pawn is not a passed pawn because Black's g7 pawn can still prevent it from promoting.

Always look for ways to weaken your opponent's pawn structure and improve your own. Of course, your opponent has the same strategy!

EN PASSANT

The third special move in chess is capturing *en passant* (the first two were promoting a pawn and castling). This tricky move doesn't happen often.

En passant means "in passing" in French and only involves the pawns.

En passant capturing can only happen if a pawn is on the fifth rank and an opposing pawn on an adjacent file advances two squares forward from its original square. The pawn moving two squares forward can be captured by the pawn on the fifth rank as if it had moved only one square forward. This capture opportunity, however, only exists for one move, the move immediately after the opposing pawn advances two squares.

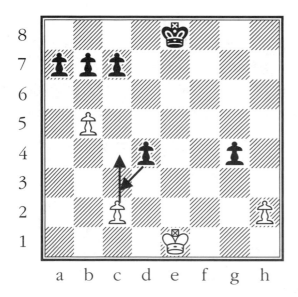

Assume it is White's move. If he plays c4, Black can capture him *en passant* by playing ...dxc3 (see diagram arrows). If White plays h4, Black can capture the h-pawn *en passant* by responding ...gxh3.

Now let's pretend that it is Black's move. If he plays ...a5, White can play bxa6. If Black plays ...c5, White can take *en passant* by bxc6. The *en passant* capture opportunity is fairly rare, unlike this example with multiple *en passant* possibilities that was chosen only to show how this special pawn move works.

Remember that because you may have the opportunity to capture *en passant* does not mean that you should automatically do so. You should always try to make moves that make sense and improve your position.

Basset Hound Problems

 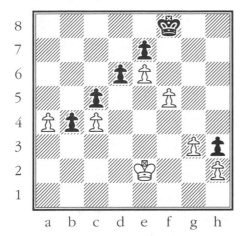

Which pawns are protected passed pawns?

_____

 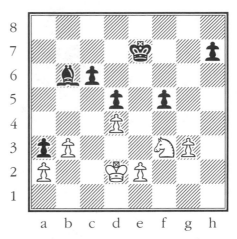

Which pawns are isolated?

_____

 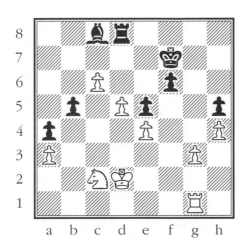

Which pawns are backward pawns?

_____

 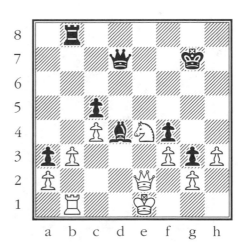

Which pawns are base pawns?

_____

8-5

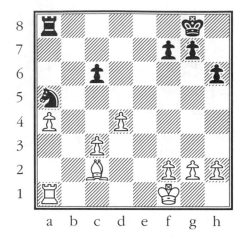

What type of pawn is the pawn on a4?

_____

8-6

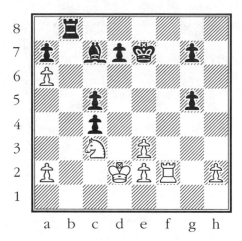

How many sets of doubled isolated pawns are on the board?

_____

8-7

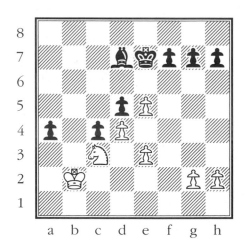

Which pawn is the strongest?

_____

8-8

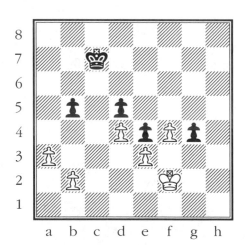

**Black to move.
Which pawn is the weakest?**

_____

 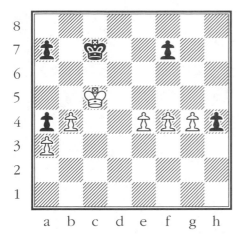

8-9

Which pawn is the strongest?

_____

 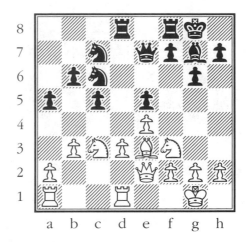

8-10

Which pawn is the weakest?

_____

Chess Detective Problems

 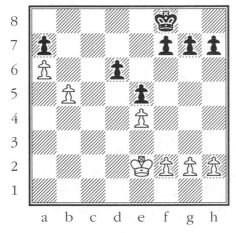

8-11

What is White's best move?

1._____

 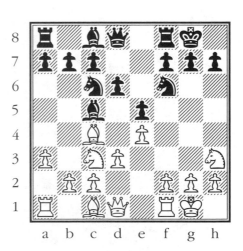

8-12

What is Black's best move?

1..._____

 # 8-13

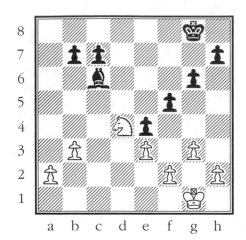

What is White's best move?

1._____

 # 8-14

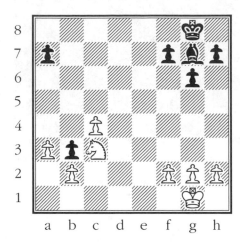

What is Black's best move?

1..._____

 # 8-15

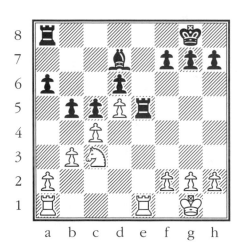

What is White's best move?

1._____

 # 8-16

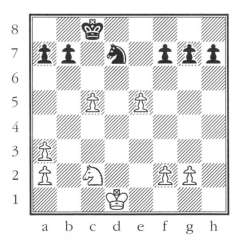

Which pawn should Black capture?

1..._____

8-17

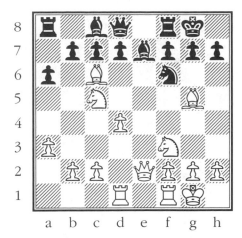

With which pawn should Black capture the bishop on c6?

1..._____

8-18

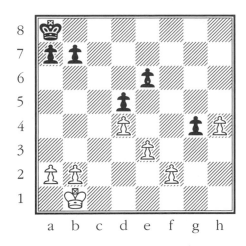

White moved his h2 pawn to h4. What is Black's best move?

1..._____

8-19

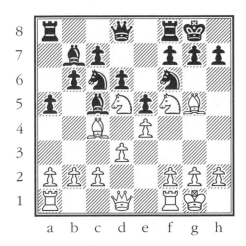

What is White's best move?

1._____

8-20

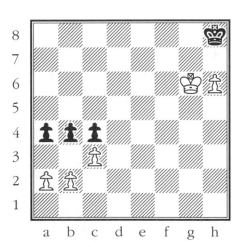

What is Black's best move?

1..._____

LESSON 9

SQUARE OF THE PAWN

...Chess is "a lot like football because you have to set up your offense and your defense, every once in a while you need to give up a piece of your team in order to make the big play. It's a game of patience, and that pretty much defines how I run the ball. I'm patient, always looking for the opportunity and always trying to capitalize on the other person's mistake."

Priest Holmes
All-Pro National Football League Running Back

The square of the pawn is a basic chess concept that applies to most chess endgames. The goal and dream of every pawn is get to the other side of the board and promote, usually to a queen. The pawns become more valuable in the endgame since most of the opponent's pieces that can block or capture the pawns on their way to their promotion square have been captured. The square of the pawn is an imaginary square that the opposing king must get into in order to win a race with a passed pawn that is trying to promote. The square is defined on the side of the pawn where the defending king is.

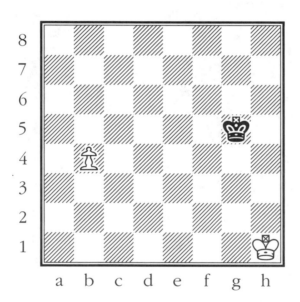

Black has insufficient mating material. White's only chance to win is to promote the passed b-pawn. His king is too far away to help out. The question is whether or not the pawn can advance to b8 before the Black king can catch it. Pawns and kings run the same speed, one square at a time.

First, let's define the square of the pawn. The four corners of the square of the pawn are: the square the pawn is currently resting on; the promotion square; the square on the diagonal drawn to the eighth rank from pawn's current position (which creates a right triangle); and the square on the board diagonally opposite from the promotion square that completes the imaginary square. The three corners (not including the square that pawn is currently on) are shown with stars below. If the Black king can get into the square, he can capture the pawn and draw the game.

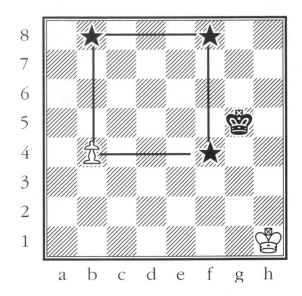

The square of a White pawn is marked with the stars.

If it is White's move, he plays 1.b5, shrinking the square. The new corners of the square of the pawn are at b5, b8, e8, and e5. Black can play 1...Kf6, but he can't make up time and get into the square of the pawn. White will win the race, promote the pawn and checkmate with the king and queen.

If it is Black to move, he plays 1...Kf6 (or 1...Kf5 or 1...Kf4) and he gets into the square of the passed pawn, runs down the pawn and captures it, and then claims a draw by insufficient mating material.

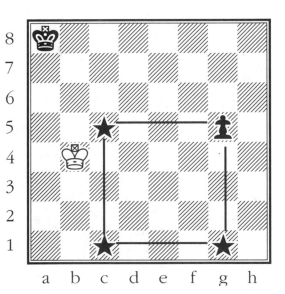

The square of a Black pawn is marked with the stars.

In the position at the bottom of the last page, Black is ahead a pawn, which is moving down, not up like the White pawn in the previous example.

White can draw if it is his move…the White king enters the square of the passed pawn by moving to the c-file. Black wins if it is his move. He advances his pawn to g4 and the White king cannot enter the square and catch up to it.

Consider this endgame position with Black to move.

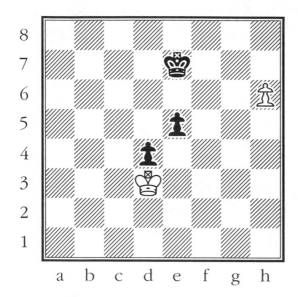

Black to move.

The White king is solidly in the square of both Black's passed pawns. The corners of the square of the White passed pawn are h6, h8, f8, and f6. Black must move his king to the f-file to get into the square of the White pawn with, say, **1…Kf7**. Realizing that his h-pawn can't outrun the Black king to h8, White responds **2.Ke4**. Notice that the White king cannot capture the pawn on e5 because he would leave the square of the Black pawn on d4. Black can respond by playing **2…Kg6**. White is lost. The Black king can walk over and capture the White pawn and then come back toward the center of the board and help escort his pawns up the board. The White king can only watch as his pawn gets captured, since he cannot leave the square of the d4 pawn (d4, d1, g1, g4).

Another way to think about it is the White king must stay and baby-sit the Black pawns. Pretend the square of the passed pawn is a house. What happens if the babysitter leaves the house…she gets in big trouble when mom and dad come home!

Consider this position with Black to move.

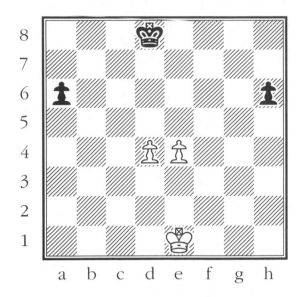

Black to move.

First let's pick up the clues in the position. Black has isolated passed pawns on a6 and h6. White has two connected passed pawns on d4 and e4. At the moment both kings are in the square of the other player's pawns.

1...a5 The White king is still in the square of the a5 pawn. Note that there are several ways for Black to win this position by advancing his pawns. Black could also play 1...h5.

2. e5 White pushes his passed pawn.

2...a4 Now the White king is out of the square of the a-pawn.

3.Kd2 Getting back into the square.

3...h5! The White king is about to have a big problem...he cannot stay in the square of both Black pawns and one of them will promote to a queen. The Black king can stop the White pawns, if they make a run for it.

Basset Hound Problems

Make a star on the corners of squares of the passed pawns in the positions below. You don't need to star the corner that the pawn is on.

 **9-1**

 **9-2**

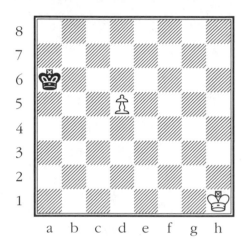

 **9-3**

 **9-4**

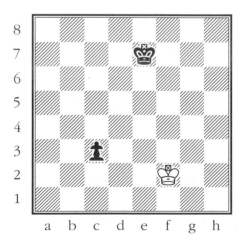

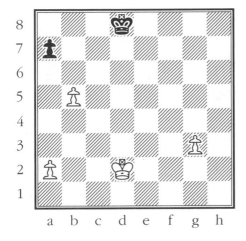

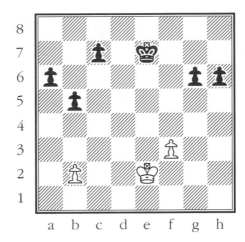

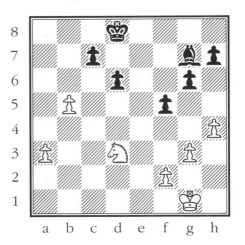

9-9

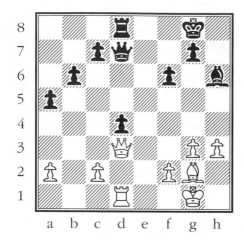

9-10

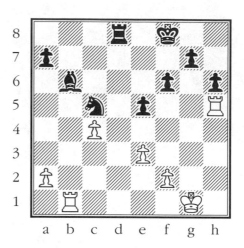

Chess Detective Problems

9-11

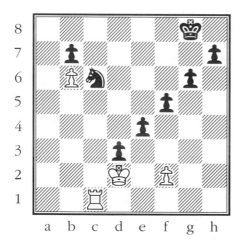

What is White's winning move?

1._____

9-12

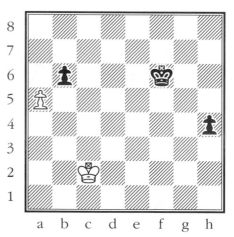

What is White's winning move?

1._____

 **9-13**

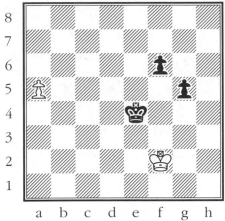

What is Black's winning move?

1..._____

 **9-14**

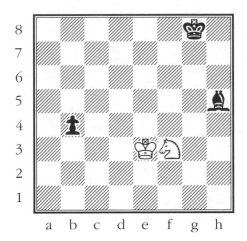

What is Black's winning move?

1..._____

 **9-15**

Black moved his pawn from g7 to g5. What is White's winning move?

1._____

 **9-16**

What is White's winning move?

1._____

 **9-17**

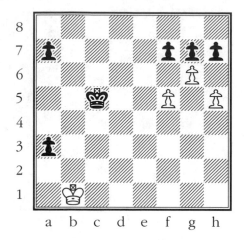

What is Black's winning move?

1..._____

 **9-18**

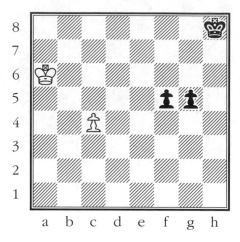

What is Black's winning move?

1..._____

 **9-19**

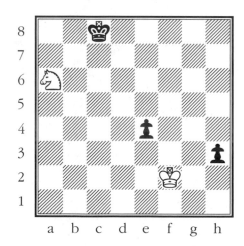

What is Black's winning move?

1..._____

 **9-20**

What is White's winning move?

1._____

LESSON 10

CHECKMATE PATTERNS

". . . and they lived happily ever after."

Back Rank Mate (a review of Lesson 4)

Remember that ranks are rows, numbered by counting from your side of the board, and that from Black's perspective this numbering system is the opposite of that used for algebraic notation. Pawns start on the second rank and promote to queens on the eighth rank. The first rank (where your pieces start) is commonly called the back rank. A back rank checkmate occurs when the king is on the back rank, trapped by his own pawns since they prevent him from escaping to the second rank in the event of a check. The opponent's rook or queen then moves to the eighth rank, and puts the king in checkmate.

With White to move, he plays 1.Rd8 mate. Normally a back rank mate occurs when one of the players doesn't look at his opponent's threats. Remember, before you make your move, always check to see what your opponent can do to you.

If it were Black to move, he could avoid mate by playing …Rc8 to protect the back rank or …Kf8 so that the king could escape to e7. It is a good idea to centralize the king in the endgame because the king is a powerful piece and most of the opposing pieces are traded off, so the chances of a checkmate in the middle of the board are slim. Black could also move any of the pawns in front of his king to create a flight square.

Smothered Mate

Although the smothered mate does not occur as often as the back rank mate, it is a common enough mating pattern to have its own name.

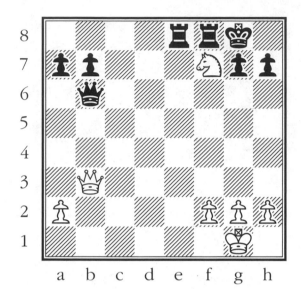

With Black to move he will back rank White by playing 1...Re1 mate.

Let's pretend it is White to move. Black is way ahead in material (a seven-pawn advantage...two rooks for a knight). White looks to be in trouble, but notice that the White queen, knight, and Black king are all lined up on the same diagonal.

If the knight moves, there will be a discovered check from the White queen to the Black king. Can you find a double check? **1.Nh6+** The White queen and the White knight both put the Black king in check. When a player is in double check, he must move his king because capturing either piece or blocking one of the checks doesn't work since there are two attackers. Black is forced to play **1...Kh8**. Now White sacrifices his queen by playing **2.Qg8+!** A sacrifice is when you give up material voluntarily in order to gain a greater advantage. In this case the queen is sacrificed to force checkmate. The Black king cannot capture the queen because the knight defends her. The only other choice for Black that gets him out of check is **2...Rxg8**.

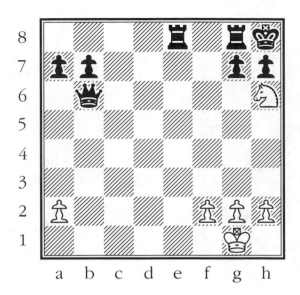

Now White plays **3.Nf7 mate**. This is called a smothered mate because Black's king is smothered by his other pieces and cannot escape.

Here is a collection of other checkmate patterns. Find the checkmate move in each diagram below. It is White to move in each of these examples. The answer and an explanation of mate is given below each diagram.

Rh1 mate

The White queen controls the g7, g8, and h7 flight squares. The rook attacks and checkmates the Black king.

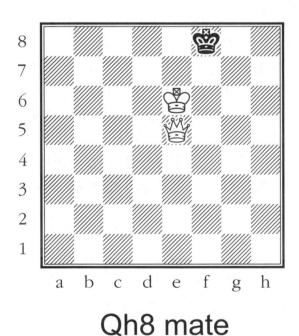

Qh8 mate

The White queen puts the Black king in check and controls the flight squares e8, g7, and g8. The White king attacks the e7 and f7 flight squares.

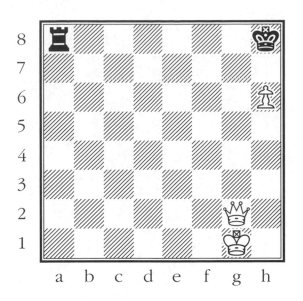

Qg7 mate

The White queen attacks the king and controls the flight squares g8 and h7. The pawn on h6 protects her.

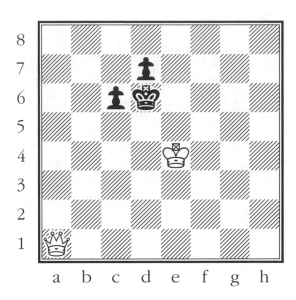

Qe5 mate

The White queen attacks the king and controls the flight squares c5, c7, d5, e6, and e7. The king protects her.

Ra7 mate

The White rook attacks the king and controls the b7 flight square. The knight protects the rook and attacks b8.

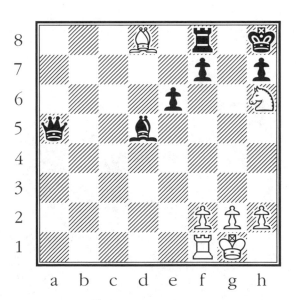

Bf6 mate

The White bishop attacks the king and controls the g7 flight square. The knight attacks g8.

147

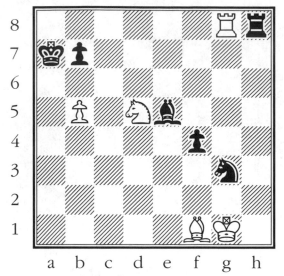

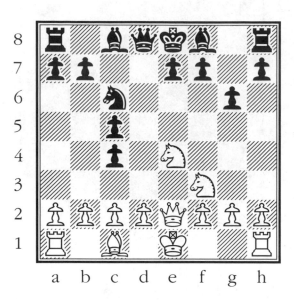

b6 mate

The pawn checks the king and is protected by the knight. The White rook attacks a8 and b8. The White bishop attacks a6.

Nf6 mate

The knight attacks the king and the d7 square. The Black pawn on e7 cannot capture the knight because it is pinned to the king by the White queen.

Basset Hound Problems
Mate in 1 problems

 10-1

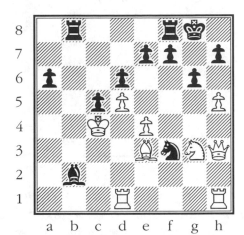

What Black move checkmates White?

1..._____

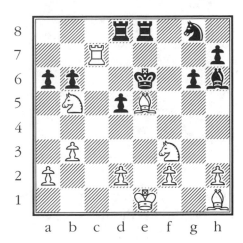 10-2

What White move checkmates Black?

1._____

 10-3

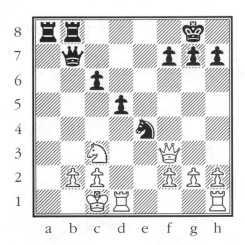

How many ways can Black checkmate White on the next move? What are the moves?

_____

 10-4

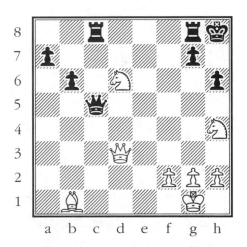

How many ways can White checkmate Black on the next move? What are the checkmate moves?

_____

10-5

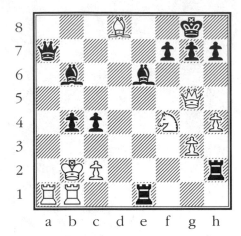

How many ways can Black checkmate White on the next move? What are the moves?

_____

10-6

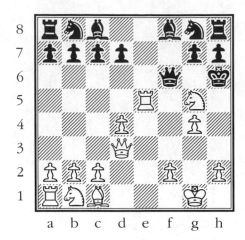

How many ways can White checkmate Black on the next move? What are the checkmate moves?

_____

 # 10-7

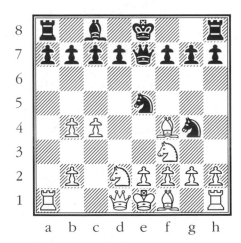

What Black move checkmates White?

1..._____

 # 10-8

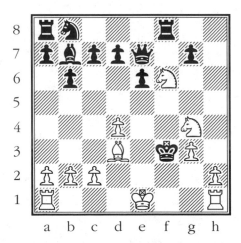

White has not moved his king or rooks. What White move checkmates Black?

1._____

 **10-9**

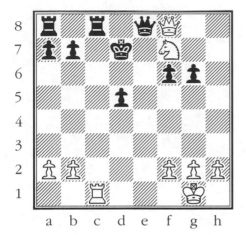

What White move checkmates Black?

1._____

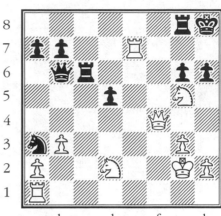 **10-10**

What White move checkmates Black?

1._____

Chess Detective Problems
Mate in 2 problems

 10-11

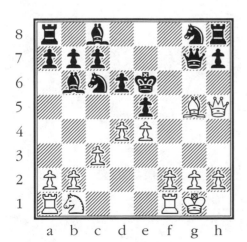

White to move and mate in two.

1._____ + _____   2._____mate

 10-12

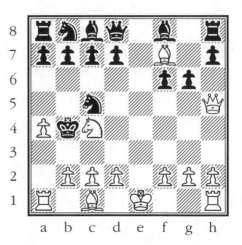

White to move and mate in two.

1._____ + _____   2._____mate

151

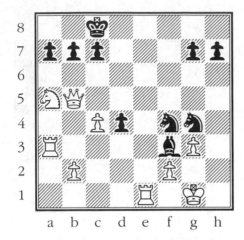

10-13

Black to move and mate in two.

1... _____+ 2._____ _____ mate

 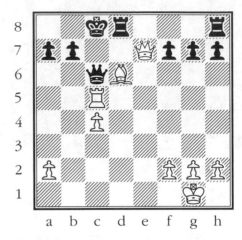

10-14

White to move and mate in two.

1._____ + _____ 2._____mate

 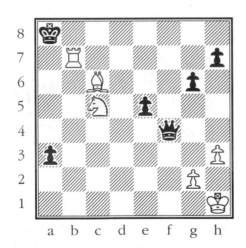

10-15

White to move and mate in two.

1._____+ _____ 2._____mate

10-16

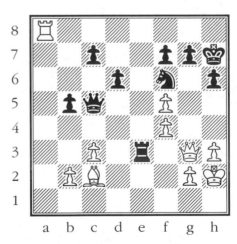

White to move and mate in two.

1._____+ _____ 2._____mate

10-17

10-18

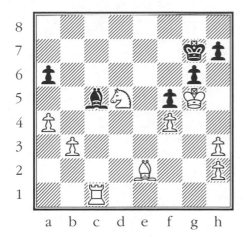

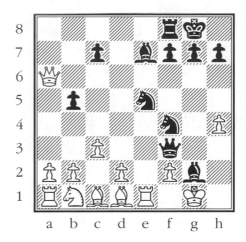

Black to move and mate in two.

1... _____+   2._____ _____ mate

Black to move and mate in two.

1... _____+   2._____ _____ mate

10-19

10-20

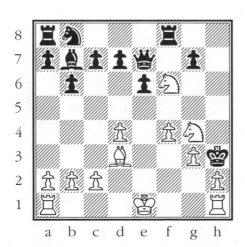

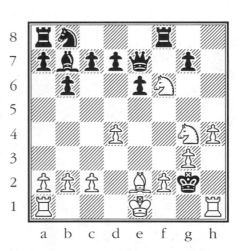

White to move and mate in two.

1._____+ _____   2._____mate

White to move and mate in two.

1._____ + _____   2._____mate

   or   2._____mate

APPENDIX A

CHESS PUZZLES

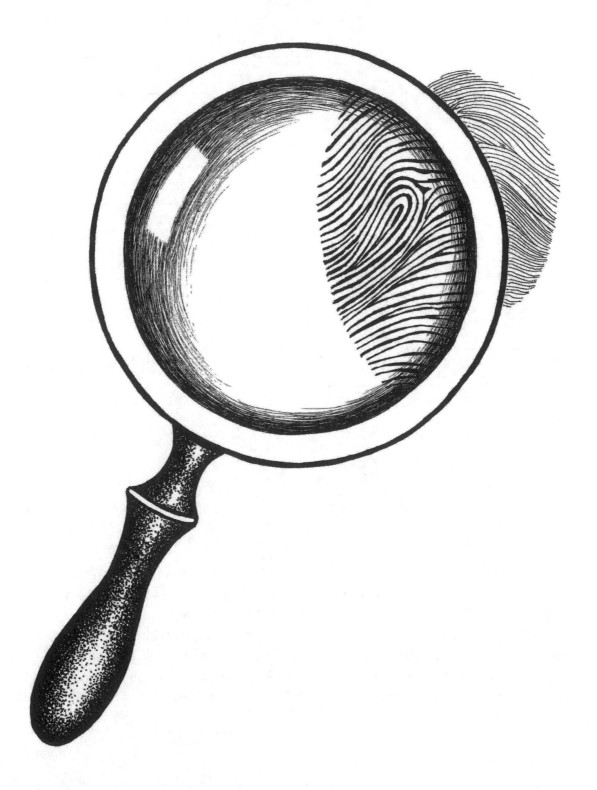

Basset Hound

Across

2. The object of the game
4. 64 of these
5. Worth 5 points
7. Piece that cannot be captured
9. Moves diagonally, worth 3 points
10. The player who moves first
11. When the king is attacked
14. The most powerful piece

Down

1. The player who moves second
2. Moving the king and rook in one move
3. Can promote to a queen
6. When the game ends a tie
7. The only piece that jumps
8. Attacking two pieces at once
12. e4, e5, d4, d5
13. When an attacked piece shields one of greater value

(Solution on page 179)

Chess Detective

Across
1. a-, b-, c-, and d- files
6. Falls when you run out of time
8. Special pawn move
9. When none of a player's pieces can move
10. Pins, forks, and skewers are these
12. e-, f-, g-, and h- files
13. Chess name for columns

Down
2. When only few pieces are left on the board
3. Moving bishops and knights into the game
4. The early moves of the game
5. When a pawn changes into a queen
7. A pawn all by himself
11. When an attacked piece shields one of less value

(Solution on page 179)

Chess Terms

Find and circle the words below

B	C	N	R	D	Y	U	I	J	B	R	F	M	V	A	G
S	T	A	L	E	M	A	T	E	Q	L	L	U	F	O	N
P	S	G	I	K	D	F	S	P	Z	U	A	D	B	M	I
B	R	J	M	R	E	W	E	K	S	B	A	C	T	S	K
F	W	O	O	W	A	Q	G	Z	V	R	C	M	K	Z	H
G	A	B	M	L	C	A	S	T	L	I	N	G	R	O	C
V	P	A	T	O	V	P	R	C	H	D	P	I	R	H	A
P	M	U	S	L	T	D	Z	E	V	M	S	B	E	J	B
E	T	I	H	W	P	I	O	L	A	F	R	C	G	L	V
F	P	J	R	X	I	M	O	B	Y	G	K	C	A	M	O
K	G	A	W	B	G	F	I	N	K	M	O	I	L	Q	J
N	I	K	W	F	I	Z	M	N	A	B	R	W	S	W	K
I	T	U	R	N	V	U	R	T	C	E	N	S	T	A	O
G	B	V	H	C	O	J	E	T	T	Q	M	V	R	S	O
H	A	N	E	E	U	Q	M	A	G	P	A	R	U	G	R
T	O	R	D	P	B	I	M	R	P	O	H	S	I	B	T

BISHOP	PAWN
BLACK	PROMOTION
CASTLING	QUEEN
CHECKMATE	ROOK
KING	SKEWER
KNIGHT	STALEMATE
MATERIAL	WHITE

(Solution on page 180)

World Champions

Find and circle the words below

C	L	I	F	B	N	R	F	Z	T	I	N	I	E	T	S
W	A	B	Q	Z	E	M	S	I	W	G	W	N	B	R	J
C	T	C	S	H	A	M	S	P	A	S	S	K	Y	P	K
A	T	H	C	Y	Y	O	G	E	N	B	X	M	V	E	Q
U	B	S	N	S	V	K	D	H	K	R	G	O	W	T	C
S	I	J	L	X	R	F	A	Z	S	N	D	U	G	M	A
F	G	O	E	I	P	H	L	S	N	P	E	C	U	F	P
N	V	K	N	N	J	E	O	U	P	A	G	O	H	M	A
W	V	R	Y	B	I	T	T	J	X	A	M	K	Y	X	B
R	Z	A	D	E	P	H	T	R	D	Y	R	J	N	L	L
E	X	M	R	S	L	T	K	Q	O	L	K	O	S	K	A
K	Y	N	K	Y	S	A	N	E	Z	S	G	Z	V	F	N
S	R	I	O	H	U	G	J	A	L	M	I	H	R	P	C
A	B	K	K	D	R	I	C	E	M	A	T	A	O	S	A
L	O	O	B	O	T	V	I	N	N	I	K	M	N	I	Z
B	P	N	C	T	V	O	P	R	A	K	V	D	Y	X	G

STEINITZ   TAL
LASKER   PETROSIAN
CAPABLANCA   SPASSKY
ALEKHINE   FISCHER
EUWE   KARPOV
BOTVINNIK   KASPAROV
SMYSLOV   KRAMNIK

(Solution on page 180)

APPENDIX B

SOLUTIONS TO PROBLEMS

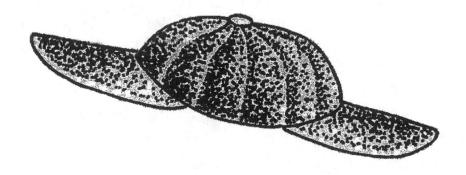

Chapter 1

 Basset Hound Solutions

1-1   9 + 5 + 3 + 3 = 20

1-2   1 + 3 + 1+ 3 + 3 + 5 = 16

1-3

King	e1	Bishop	f3
Queen	d5	Knight	c3
Rook	a1	Pawn	h5

1-4

King	g8	Bishop	b4
Queen	c7	Knight	f6
Rook	h1	Pawn	d4

1-5   The bishop can move to h5, g4, h1, g2, e4, d5, or capture the Black pawn on c6.

1-6   The knight can capture either the rook on d6 or the bishop on c3. Note that when the knight is on b5, it is attacked by both the pawn on a4 and the queen on b8.

1-7   The bishop on a2 is checking the Black king.

1-8   No. White's king can move safely to g1. Black could then checkmate him on the next move by playing …Re1 mate.

1-9   White's king can move to f1, f2, or g2.

1-10   Because Black touched the pawn on c4, he must capture it, since he can legally. Therefore, he must play 1…Qxc4. White can then recapture with 2.bxc4 and win the Black queen.

 Chess Detective Solutions

1-11   White has more material. He is ahead by one point (a bishop plus a knight is worth six points and a rook is worth five).

1-12   White cannot move his king to f1 because of the bishop on a6. Therefore, his only choice is to capture the queen on h2 with his king. After capturing the queen, White will then be ahead by two points (queen minus bishop, knight, and pawn, or 9 − 3 − 3 − 1 = 2).

1-13   The rook, on a8

1-14   12 (Rook + Bishop + Knight + Pawn)

1-15   Yes, trading the bishop for the knight is a good idea because White is 3 points up in material and it is usually a good idea to trade pieces when you are ahead.

1-16   …Bb7+, …Bf5+, …Rd4+, …Re8+, …f5+, …Nf6+

1-17   Qa2+, Qb3+, Bc4+, Bg6+, Rf1+, Rf3+

1-18   No, because he can play …b3, blocking the check from the a2 bishop. On the next move, White could then play Bxb3 mate because none of the other Black pieces can block the check and the Black king has no escape squares.

1-19   No, he cannot capture the Black queen with 1.Qxc5. He must play 1.Kh2, his only king move. If he said, "I adjust", before touching the king, he wouldn't be forced to move it and could instead capture the Black queen.

1-20   Because Black cannot legally capture the pawn on g2, he is free to play something else like 1…Bxc2, capturing the White queen. He should be careful in the future what he touches…next time he may not be so lucky!

Chapter 2

 ## Basset Hound Solutions

2-1   No, 1.Nh3 is not a good move because "A knight on the rim is dim." The f3 square is a much better square for the knight because it attacks the center.

2-2   No, because a5 is on the edge of the board, not the center, and it does not help a bishop develop.

2-3   The e5 square is the most important of these squares because it is one of the four center squares.

2-4   The bishop is best placed on the c4 square since it controls the center. If the bishop moves to d3, it blocks the d2 pawn from moving toward the center. If it moves to a6, it can be captured by Black's b7 pawn or b8 knight.

2-5   Moving the pawn to d4 is the best because it attacks the center. White will not lose material because the pawn is attacked twice and protected twice. Moving the pawn to d3, is a bit passive and partially blocks in the bishop on f1.

2-6   Moving the knight to f6 is best because it attacks two center squares (e4 and d5). If the knight moves to e7, it blocks the bishop on f8. Remember that if it moves to h6, "A knight on the rim is dim."

2-7   Moving the queen to f3 is a bad move because it brings the queen out too early and blocks the knight on g1 from developing to its best square on f3.

2-8   The best move of these choices is 3.c3 because it blocks the check and chases away the bishop gaining time (a tempo, in chess terms). 3.Ke2 moves the king so White will lose the right to castle later and blocks the bishop on f1 from developing. 3.Qd2 is a really bad move because Black could then play 3...Bxd2+, winning the queen for a bishop.

2-9   No, 2.d3 is not a good move because it blocks in the bishop on f1 from developing to an active square. It would be better to play d3 after the bishop developed to either c4 or b5.

2-10   Ne5 is not a terrible move, but it isn't a good move either because the knight moved a second time before White developed his other minor pieces.

 # Chess Detective Solutions

2-11   White is threatening both 4.Qxf7 mate and 4.Qxe5+, winning the e5 pawn. Black can play 4...Qe7 or 4...Qf6 to defend both threats.

2-12   2.d4 is the best move of these choices because it controls the center. 2.Bd3 is bad because it blocks the d2 pawn. 2.Bb5 is okay, but the bishop will likely get chased back by one of Black's pawns. 2.Be2 is passive.

2-13   The light-squared bishop on c8 will be the most difficult to develop to a good square because it is blocked in by pawns. The knight on b8 won't have problems developing because it can jump over the Black pawns.

2-14   Usually castling kingside is a good idea, but not in this case because White has moved up his pawns on the kingside and the king will be open to direct attack from the Black pieces if he tries to live there. White's best plan is to develop his queen and his bishop on c1 and then castle queenside, using the queenside pawns (which haven't moved) for protection.

2-15   3.Nc3 is the best of these choices for White because it develops a piece and protects the e4 pawn which is being attacked by the pawn on d5. 3.Nf3 and 3.Bf4 will both lose the pawn on e4. 3.Qf3 defends the pawn on e4, but brings the queen out too early and blocks the knight from moving to f3.

2-16   At first glance, 2...Nc6 looks like a good move. But notice that White can play 3.b5 to chase the knight away so he can then capture the e5 pawn with the bishop. Then Black's only way to try to save the pawn is 3...Nd4, blocking the bishop's threat while attacking White's b-pawn. White could then play 4.e3 attacking the knight again and protecting the b5 pawn with the bishop on f1. After the Black knight moves, White would then win the pawn on e5. Chess masters must think several moves ahead like this to see possible future positions.

2-17   Playing 5.gxf5 would win a bishop, but White has opened up his king and Black could then play 5...Qh4 mate!

2-18   Black has won a pawn, but is quickly falling behind in development. He should play 4...Nxc3 to trade off one of White's developed pieces and not lose more time. After 4...Nc5, White plays 5.Nxe5 with a lead in development and an attack. 4...Bd6 defends the pawn, but loses the knight to 5.Nxe4. 4...d5 protects the knight, but White has two attackers on the d5 pawn with only the queen to defend it. White could comfortably play either 5.Nxd5 or 5.Bxd5 regaining the pawn with an attack.

2-19   No, 2...d5 is not a good move because if White plays 3.exd5 and Black were to recapture with 3...Qxd5, White could gain a tempo by developing a piece and attacking the queen at the same time with 4.Nc3.

2-20   Yes, because Black would have to respond ...Kxd8 and wouldn't be able to castle later in the game because his king has moved.

Chapter 3

 Basset Hound Solutions

3-1   7...0-0
3-2   12.Nd3
3-3   25...Re8
3-4   42...Rxg3+
3-5   65.Rg3+
3-6   73...Qxa6+
3-7   8...cxd4
3-8   17...0-0-0
3-9   27.Rxd5+
3-10   39.axb5

 Chess Detective Solutions

3-11   4...Nfd7
3-12   7.Ndf3
3-13   11...N5f6 (both knights are on the d-file...so 11...Ndf6 doesn't work)
3-14   15.N3xd4 (both knights are on the f-file...so 15.Nfxd4 doesn't work)
3-15   18...Ned7
3-16   19.Rfd1
3-17   38...R8a6 (both rooks are on the a-file...so 38...Raa6 doesn't work)
3-18   48.Rcxa4
3-19   51.a8=Q
3-20   7...fxg1=N+

Chapter 4

Basset Hound Solutions

4-1   Qe7

4-2   ...Qd4

4-3   Rg3

4-4   ...Rc3

4-5   Qb7 checkmate is best. If White plays Qb8+, Black can play ...Ka6 and lives for at least one more move.

4-6   Rg1 checkmate is the best move. If Ra2+, Black plays ...Kb1. Rb2 is the worst of the three moves because it is stalemate.

4-7   Ra8 mate

4-8   Rg6+ is the best move. Black will have to move his king to h4 or h5. White can then play Rh2 mate.

4-9   Qg6 mate and Qh1 mate

4-10   ...Rd1 mate (the knight guards a2)

Chess Detective Solutions

4-11   3.Rxf7 is a bad move because Black is stalemated. White is trying to win because he is ahead in material. 43.Rxb6 is the best move, winning a pawn and giving the Black king more possible moves to reduce the chance of stalemate.

4-12   Black is way behind in material. He can play...Qxg2+! and White must recapture with the king. Notice the Black king can't move legally to any square...Stalemate!

4-13   There are 3 moves for Black that checkmate White: ...Qa1 mate, ...Qb1 mate, and ...Qf2 mate.

4-14   There are 4 moves for White that checkmate Black: Qe5 mate, Qb2 mate, Qb8 mate, and Bc3 mate.

4-15   The only checkmate move for Black is ...Rh1 mate. If Black plays ...Qh2+, White can play Kf1.

4-16 White has two moves to checkmate Black: Qa5 mate and Qg5 mate.

4-17 Black cannot checkmate White on the next move. The White queen defends the b2 square from the attempt at mate with …Qxb2. White can play Na3 to defend against …Ra8+ or …Qa6+.

4-18 White has only one way to checkmate Black on this move: Bh5 mate.

4-19 Black can checkmate White on this move two different ways: …Qg2 mate and …Qh1 mate.

4-20 White can only checkmate Black one way: Qxh7 mate.

Chapter 5

Basset Hound Solutions

5-1   1.Bf3

5-2   1.Ra6+

5-3   1…Nd4+

5-4   1…a1=Q+ (1…a1=B+ is also a skewer, but Black would rather have the queen)

5-5   1.Rc6+

5-6   1.Bc3

5-7   1…Qf1+, 1…Qf3+, 1…d5

5-8   1…Rg7

5-9   1.b8=N+

5-10 1.Qe4, 1.Re1

Chess Detective Solutions

5-11 1.d4

5-12 1.Bd3+

5-13 1.Bf3 (the bishop attacks the rook on a8 and the rook makes a discovered attack on the queen)

5-14 1…d6+! (the bishop makes a discovered attack on the queen)

5-15 1.Qg4+ (forking the king and both rooks)

5-16 1.f5. The knight is pinned to the king and is attacked three times and defended three times. 1.f5 attacks it fourth time with the pawn, which is even less valuable than the knight.

5-17 1.Qe1. If 1.Be1, then 1…Qxf4+. If 1.g3 or 1.Be3, then 1…Nxg3+ works for Black because the pawn on h2 is pinned to the rook by the Black queen (2.hxg3 Qxh1). If 1.Nh3, then 1…Bxh3 wins the knight and renews the mate threat on f2.

5-18 Taking the knight with 1.gxf3 is a bad idea because Black could play 1…Rh2 mate (the g2 pawn is pinned to the h2 square).

5-19 1…Bf5+ saves the bishop. White doesn't have time to take the queen because of the check by the bishop. After White gets out of check, Black has time to save his queen.

5-20 White can play 1.Rxg7+! followed by 2.Qxh4 winning a queen and a pawn for a rook.

Chapter 6

 Basset Hound Solutions

6-1 1.Qe3 is the best of the three moves for White. If 1.Qd6, Black is stalemated. After 1.Qb8+, Black is forced to play 1…Kxb8 and it is a draw by insufficient mating material.

6-2 1…Bc3 is the best of the three choices. White then must play 2.Ka3 and Black can play 2…Ra5 mate. 1…Kc3 and 1…Rb5 are both stalemate.

6-3 Taking the White rook off the board with 1…Rxf2 is the best move for Black because after White recaptures the rook, the game is drawn by insufficient mating material. With the rooks on the board, White has an advantage and may be able to win the game.

6-4 Taking Black's pawn with 1.Nxc6 is the best move. The pawn is the only remaining Black piece with the potential to checkmate White (if the pawn where to promote to a queen). After taking the pawn, the game is drawn by insufficient mating material.

6-5 1.Be8 is White's best choice. After 1…h5 (Black's only move), White can play 2.Bc6 mate. The other choices, 1.Bd6 and 1.Ka6 are stalemate since Black has no king or pawn moves.

6-6 1.Bxg2 is the best move, eliminating Black's potential mating material. Taking the more valuable bishop with 1.Bxf7 loses to 1…g1=Q. 1.Bc4+ can be met by 1…Bxc4 and 2…g1=Q.

6-7 1…Rh2+ is the best move of the three choices as Black is only a few moves away from completing a rook and rook roller mate. Black is ahead in material and playing to win. Both 1…Ra1 and 1…Rd5 result in a stalemate.

6-8 1.Rxb2 is the best move because it is the only way White can stop the pawn from promoting and turning into a queen. After 1.Ra3 or 1.Kc4, Black plays 1…b1=Q.

6-9 1.Nxf2 is the best move because White must eliminate the f2 pawn before it promotes. On the second move, White can play 2.Kxh7 and the game is drawn by insufficient mating material. If 1.Nf4+, Black can play a king move like 1…Kf5 and promote the pawn the next move. If 1.Kxh7, 1…f1=Q wins for Black.

6-10 White should play 1.Kxc7 stalemate. If he tries to win by promoting the pawn by playing 1.h5, Black saves the bishop and stops the pawn by playing 1…Bf4. The Black king will then escape from the corner and start winning the White pawns.

 Chess Detective Solutions

6-11 1…Rc5 pins the White rook to the king and Black can trade rooks the next move. The game will be drawn by insufficient mating material.

6-12 1.Rb2! draws which is good for White because he is behind three pawns. 1…Rxb2 is stalemate and any other move by Black loses his rook. White can win the endgame if he is ahead a rook.

6-13 White is in trouble because he cannot stop the pawn on b2 from promoting without giving up the queen. He can save the game with a three-move repetition draw by playing 1.Qe8+ Kh7 2.Qh5+ Kg8 3.Qe8+ Kh7 4.Qh5+ Kg8 5.Qe8+

6-14 Black's best move is 1...Nd6+ forking the king and pawn. On the next move he can capture the pawn, leaving White with insufficient mating material. If Black goes for more material by playing 1...Ne7+ 2.Kd7 Nxg6 winning the bishop, the pawn promotes to a queen and White is winning.

6-15 Even though at the moment Black is behind in material, he should refuse the draw offer and play 1...b2 or 1...a2. He will soon promote a pawn to a queen and be ahead in material with a winning position.

6-16 White is behind a queen to a knight and a pawn and is, therefore, in big trouble. He can continuously check Black's king from d5, a5, or d8. For example, White can get a three-move repetition draw by playing 1.Qd5+ Qab7 2.Qa5+ Q8a7 3.Qd8+ and so on.

6-17 Black can go for checkmate by playing 1...Nd6 (or 1...Ne7 and 2...Ng6 mate). No matter which pawn White moves on the next turn, Black can play 2...Nf7 mate. If White captures the pawn on b6 with 1...Nxb6, then 2.c8=Q+ Nxc8 stalemate. Of course Black would be in trouble if he allows White to promote one of the pawns and have time to start checking him with the new queen.

6-18 Black is behind a bishop and his king and pawns cannot move. Instead of risking the loss, he can play 1...Rf7+!. White is forced to play 2.Rxf7 stalemate. If he moves the king with say, 2.Kg6, Black plays 2...Rxd7 and is ahead in material with a winning position.

6-19 White can force an insufficient mating material draw by playing 1.Rd1+ Kc5 2.Rxd6 Kxd6 3.Kxc4.

6-20 White, who is behind in material, should refuse the draw and play 1.Bh6 threatening 2.Qg7 mate which cannot be stopped (For example, 1.Bh6 Qb2 2.Qxb2 e5 3.Qxe5 f6 4.Qxf6 and 5.Qg7 mate). 1.Bb2 also threatens 2.Qg7 mate, but Black can play 1...Qxb2 giving up the queen for a bishop, avoiding mate, and remaining ahead in material.

Chapter 7

Basset Hound Solutions

7-1 The pawn on a6 can be captured by the White knight. The knight on b7 isn't "free stuff" because the bishop on g2 protects it.

7-2　The White queen can capture the pawn on h7. The other attacked pieces are defended. Note that if it were Black's move, he could play ...Qxd3 winning a free queen.

7-3　Black can play ...axb4 and win the pawn. The other attacked pawns are all defended.

7-4　Black can play ...Bxb2 and win the pawn. The other attacked pawns are all defended.

7-5　White can play Rxh6 and win the pawn. The other attacked pawns are all defended.

7-6　White can play Qxa4 and win the pawn. Everything else that White attacks is defended.

7-7　Black can play ...Rxh2 and win the pawn. Everything else that Black attacks is defended.

7-8　There isn't any "free stuff" for Black. White has everything protected.

7-9　White can win "free stuff" by playing either Rxf7+ or Bxg5. Both immediately win a pawn. Don't take the first thing you see, you may find better "free stuff."

7-10　White can either play Bxc6 winning a pawn or Qxb6 winning the knight. He should take the knight with Qxb6 because it is more valuable.

 Chess Detective Solutions

7-11　White should play 1.Bxd6 winning the pawn. Black shouldn't play 1...Rxd6 because the White queen protects the bishop.

7-12　The c5 pawn is attacked twice, defended once. White wins "free stuff" by playing 1.dxc5 dxc5 2.Bxc5.

7-13　The h3 pawn is attacked twice, defended once. Black wins "free stuff" by playing 1...Bxh3 and White cannot capture the bishop with his king because the queen defends it.

7-14　There is no "free stuff" for Black. White has all his pieces defended (the pawn on d4 is attacked three times, defended three times). Remember to win "free stuff" you usually must have more pieces attacking than your opponent has defending.

7-15 White can win the knight by playing 1.Bxf6. The pawn on g7 cannot recapture the bishop because it is pinned to the king by the White queen.

7-16 White can win the Black rook by playing 1.Qxc6. Black cannot recapture with 1...Rxc6 because of 2.Re8 mate.

7-17 White can win a pawn by playing 1.bxa3. Note that the Black pawn on d5 is attacked three times, defended only once. But White would lose material with 1.Rxd5 Nxd5 2.Qxd5 because the rook is worth more than a pawn and a knight.

7-18 Black can win "free stuff" by capturing the undefended queen with 1...Qxc2, the knight with 1...bxc3, the pawn on d4 with 1...Rxd4, or the pawn on a5 with 1...Bxa5. But the best move is 1...Qxg2 mate! (After all, the king is the best "free stuff" of all!)

7-19 White can play 1.Bxf7+!, forcing Black to play 1...Kxf7. White then wins the queen with 2.Qxd8. 1.bxc3 recaptures a pawn, but leaves White behind a knight.

7-20 White wins the knight after 1.Qd5, forking the knight and the pawn on f7, which can be captured by the queen with mate! If 1...Ng5 protecting f7, White just plays 2.Bxg5 capturing the knight for free by renewing the mate threat on f7. Forking two pieces is a way to win "free stuff." Note that 1.Qf3 does not work because Black can play 1...d5. Notice that 1.Bxf7+ Kxf7 2.Qd5+ wins back the piece and leaves White up a pawn.

Chapter 8

Basset Hound Solutions

8-1   The protected passed pawns are on b4 and g3.

8-2   The isolated pawns are on a3, f5, g3, and h7.

8-3   The backward pawns are on b5, f6, and g3.

8-4   The base pawns are on a2, f4, and g2.

8-5   The pawn on a4 is an isolated passed pawn.

8-6   There are three sets of doubled isolated pawns: a2 and a6; e2 and e3; g5 and g7. The pawns on c4 and c5 are not isolated because of the pawn on d7.

8-7   The pawn on c4 is the strongest pawn because it is a protected passed pawn. The pawn on a4 is an isolated passed pawn.

8-8   The weakest pawn on the board is Black's isolated pawn on g4. The White king can move up and take it. The pawn on b5 is also isolated, but the Black king is close enough to defend it.

8-9   The strongest pawn on the board is Black's isolated passed pawn on h4. It is ready to move forward and promote to a queen.

8-10 The weakest pawn on the board is the backward pawn on d3. Black's rooks can double up on the d-file to attack it. His other pieces can also attack it.

 Chess Detective Solutions

8-11 White's best move is 1.b6 creating a passed pawn. 1.b6 axb6 2.a7 and White's passed a-pawn will promote. If Black doesn't capture the pawn, White can play either 2.bxa7 or 2.b7 and promote the pawn the next move.

8-12 Black's best move is 1...Bxh3. White will have to recapture the bishop with 2.gxh3 and White is left with doubled isolated pawns on the h-file.

8-13 White's best move is 1.Nxc6 and Black will have to recapture with 1...bxc6. This leaves Black with doubled isolated c-pawns. White's pawn on a2 is now a dangerous passed pawn.

8-14 Black should play 1...Bxc3 and when White recaptures with 1...bxc3, he will have doubled isolated c-pawns. More importantly, the Black pawn on b3 will be a passed pawn and can promote to a queen in two moves.

8-15 White best move is 1.Rxe5. After 1...dxe5, White has a protected, passed pawn on d5.

8-16 The best pawn for Black to capture is the pawn on e5 because the c5 pawn is isolated. It is better to leave White with the weaker of the two pawns.

8-17 Black should recapture with the d-pawn. The bishop on c8 can then develop. If Black plays 1...bxc6, although the b-pawn now attacks a square in the center, the a6 pawn is now isolated.

8-18 Black's best move is capturing the h-pawn *en passant* with 1...gxh3, creating a passed h-pawn.

8-19 White's best move is capturing the knight on f6 with 1.Bxf6. If Black recaptures with 1...gxf6, he doubles his f-pawns and also opens up the Black king. White can take advantage by playing 2.Qg4+ Kh8 3.Qg7 mate. If Black doesn't recapture, he loses the knight for free and still has an exposed king.

8-20 Black's best move is 1...a3 threatening to create a passed pawn with 2...axb2. If 2.bxa3, Black can create a passed pawn by playing 2...b3 or 2...bxc3. Both players will get passed pawns on the queenside, but Black will win because his pawn is closer to promoting. Notice that the Black king blocks White's passed pawn on h6.

Chapter 9

 Basset Hound Solutions

9-1   Stars on d8, g8, and g5.

9-2   Stars on d8, a8, and a5.

9-3   Stars on h1, d1, and d5.

9-4   Stars on c1, e1, and e3.

9-5   Stars on g8, b8, and b3.

9-6   Stars on h1, c1, and c6.

9-7   For the White pawn: stars on c8, f8, and f5.
        For the Black pawn: stars on g1, d1, and d4.

9-8   For the White pawn: stars on a8, f8, and f3.
        For the Black pawn: stars on d1, h1, and h6. Notice that the square of the Black pawn is actually a rectangle. Technically, the corners would be d1, i1, and i6. Since there isn't an i-file, replace i1 and i6 with h1 and h6.

9-9   There are no passed pawns in this position.

9-10   For the White pawn on c4: stars on c8, g8, and g4.

         For the Black pawn on h6: stars on h1, c1, and c6.

 # Chess Detective Solutions

9-11   White's winning move is 1.Rxc6! After 1...bxc6, the b6 pawn is a passed pawn. White will win because the Black king is not in the square of the b6 pawn.

9-12   The White king is not in the square of the Black pawn on h4 and the Black king is not in the square of White's pawn. It is a race to the promotion squares. White should play 1.a6 h3 2.a7 h2 3.a8=Q which protects the h1 promotion square. If 1.axb6?, then 1...h3 2.b7 h2 3.b8=Q h1=Q. White got the first queen, but there aren't any squares he can use to skewer the Black king and queen to win the queen.

9-13   Black should play 1...Kd5! to get into the square of the pawn. He will have time to run over and capture the a-pawn and then come back to help his passed pawns. With the black pawns on f6 and g5, the White king will not be able to capture the f6 pawn while the Black king is on the queenside because he will leave the square of the g5 pawn.

9-14   Black should play 1...Bxf3. If White captures the bishop with 2.Kxf3, his king leaves the square of Black's passed pawn on b4. If instead of capturing the bishop, the White king goes after the pawn, the bishop can protect it.

9-15   White should capture the pawn *en passant* by playing 1.fxg6+. When Black recaptures with 1...Kxg6, his king will leave the square of the passed c-pawn.

9-16   White's winning move is 1.Qxb5+! (not 1.Nxb5? Qf1 mate). Then 1...Qxb5 2.Nxb5 Kxb5 3.h4 (moving two squares forward!) and the Black king can not get into the square of the pawn.

9-17   Black wins with 1...fxg6 2.h6 gxh6 3.f6 Kd6 and the Black king is in the square of the passed White f-pawn. Losing is 1...hxg6? 2.f6 gxf6 3.h6 and the Black king is not in the square of White's passed h-pawn.

9-18   The Black king is in the square of the White pawn, but the White king can help escort in the c-pawn if Black's king tries to stop it. Therefore, Black must race one of his passed pawns. He should play 1...f4!

because the f-pawn will promote with check. After 2.c5 f3 3.c6 f2 4.c7 f1=Q+ 5.Kb7 Black can play 5...Qc1 and take the pawn (or queen) the next move. Black will then win because the White king is not in the square of the g-pawn.

9-19   1...e3+! 2.Kxe3 h2 and the White king is outside the square of the h-pawn. If the White king doesn't take the e-pawn, he still can't stop both pawns. 1...h2 doesn't work because 2.Kg2 e3 3.Nb4 (or 3.Nc5) 3...e2 4.Nc2 (or 4.Nd3) and the knight can stop the pawn on e2 in time.

9-20   White wins by pinning the rook to the king with 1.Bh3. After Black breaks the pin with, say, 1...Ke5, White plays 2.Rxf5+ Nxf5 3.Bxf5 Kxf5 4.a5 and the pawn promotes because the Black king isn't in the square of the pawn. 1.Rxf5 doesn't work because of 1...Kxf5! 2.a5 Ne8 3.a6 Nc7 4.a7 Ke5 and the Black king walks over and captures the pawn.

Chapter 10

 Basset Hound Solutions

10-1   1...Ne5 mate (The knight also attacks d3.)

10-2   1.Nbd4 mate (1.Nfd4+ isn't mate because of 1...Kxe5)

10-3   Black can checkmate White in one move only one way by playing 1...Qxb2 mate. 1...Ra1+ isn't mate because of 2.Nb1.

10-4   White can checkmate Black two ways: 1.Nf7 mate and 1.Qh7 mate.

10-5   Black can checkmate White two ways: 1...c3 mate and 1...Bd4 mate.

10-6   White can checkmate Black in one move only one way by playing 1.Nf7 double checkmate (with the knight on f7 and the bishop on c1). 1.Qh3+ isn't mate because of 1...Kg6.

10-7   1...Nd3 is mate because the e2 pawn is pinned to the king by the Black queen.

10-8   White must put the king in check and take away the g2 flight square in order to checkmate Black. The only checkmate move is 1.0-0 mate.

10-9   1.Qd6 mate

10-10   1.Rh7 mate

Chess Detective Solutions

10-11 1.Qe8+ Qe7 (or 1...Nge7 or 1...Nce7) 2.d5 mate
10-12 1.c3+ Kb3 2.Qd1 mate
10-13 1...Nh3+ 2.Kf1 Nh2 mate
10-14 1.Rxc6+ bxc6 2.Qc7 mate
10-15 1.Rc7+ Kb8 2.Na6 mate
10-16 1.Qg6+! fxg6 2.fxg6 mate
10-17 1...h6+ 2.Kh4 Bf2 mate
10-18 1...Nh3+ 2.Kh2 Ng4 mate
10-19 1.Bf1+ Bg2 2.Nf2 mate
10-20 1.Rh2+ Kg1 2.0-0-0 mate or 2.Kd2 mate

Basset Hound (for page 156)

Chess Detective (for page 157)

Chess Terms Solutions (for page 158)

								B						G
S	T	A	L	E	M	A	T	E		L				N
P										A				I
	R			R	E	W	E	K	S		C			K
		O										K		
			M		C	A	S	T	L	I	N	G		C
			O									H		
			T									E		
E	T	I	H	W		I					C	L		
	P						O			K	A			
K		A					N	M		I				
N			W				A	R						K
I			N				T	E						O
G						E	T							O
H		N	E	E	U	Q		A						R
T							M	P	O	H	S	I	B	

World Champions Solutions (for page 159)

	L					R		Z	T	I	N	I	E	T	S
	A				E		S								
	T			H		M	S	P	A	S	S	K	Y		
		C		Y										E	
	S		S		K							W			C
	I		L			A					U				A
F	O	E		P			S			E					P
	V	K		N		E		P							A
	R			I		T		A							B
R	A			H		R			R						L
E	M			K		O			O						A
K	N			E		S			V						N
S	I					L		I							C
A	K					A		A							A
L		B	O	T	V	I	N	N	I	K		N			
			V	O	P	R	A	K							

GLOSSARY

absolute pin when a piece is pinned to the king and cannot move because the king would be placed in check

adjacent next to

algebraic notation chess language that describes a move by giving the moving piece and the square it moves to

analog clock a chess clock with a traditional clock face with hands and a flag which falls at the top of the hour to show that a player has run out of time

attacker a piece that attacks an opposing piece

back rank another name for the first rank, the rank closest to the player behind the pawns in the game's starting position

back rank mate a checkmate that occurs when the king is attacked on the back rank by a queen or rook and his escape is blocked by his own pawns

backward pawn a typically weak base pawn on a half-open file that may be easily attacked by the opponent's pieces, especially the rooks

base pawn the pawn in a pawn chain that is closest to the player and has no pawn to protect it

bishop (symbol – B) a piece worth three pawns that moves diagonally in any direction until it runs into another piece or the edge of the board

Black player with the dark-colored pieces who moves second in the game

Black move written in algebraic notation by giving the move number, followed by three periods, and then the move; for example 1...Nf6

capture when a piece moves to a square where an opposing piece is resting and removes that piece from the board

castling a special move that usually occurs in the opening, getting the king out of the center and developing a rook, and the only time a player can move two pieces in one turn

center the middle of the board that includes the squares e4, e5, d4, and d5

check when the king is placed under attack

checkmate the object of the game which occurs when the king is put in check and there is no way for the king to escape

combination series of moves that are played in an exact sequence to gain an advantage

consecutively one immediately following another

defender a piece that defends one of its own pieces

developing a piece (also called development) when a piece (knight, bishop, rook, or queen) moves off its starting square to a better square, increasing its power

digital clock a chess clock with a digital face (showing numbers only, no clock hands)

discovered attack moving a piece and attacking an opponent's piece with a bishop, rook, or queen hiding behind the piece that moved

discovered check moving a piece and checking the opponent's king with a bishop, rook, or queen hiding behind the piece that moved

double attack a discovered attack where the moving piece also attacks an opponent's piece

double check a discovered check where the moving piece also checks the king

doubled isolated pawns two pawns lined up vertically on the same file with no pawn on a file next to them that can protect them

doubled pawns two pawns lined up vertically on the same file that have a pawn on a file next to them that can provide protection

draw a chess game ending in a tie

draw offer when one of the players makes his move and verbally offers a draw to his opponent

endgame the part of the game when only a few pieces are still on the board

en passant ("in passing" in French) a special pawn capture that exists for only one move and occurs when a pawn on the fifth rank captures an opposing pawn on an adjacent file that advanced two squares forward as if it only moved one square forward

en prise ("in take" in French) refers to piece that can be captured

50-move draw a rare type of draw where 50 moves have taken place with no pieces being captured and no pawns moved

files columns on the chessboard identified by a letter from a to h

flag the part of an analog chess clock that falls at the top of the hour when a player has run out of time

flight square (or escape square) a square that a king can move to in order to escape checkmate

forcing move a move, like a check, giving the opponent little or no choice in his response

fork a common type of tactic that occurs when a piece attacks two or more pieces at once

free stuff another way to say hanging pieces

etiquette manners

half-open file file where one player has a pawn and the other player doesn't have a pawn

hanging a piece or pawn left unguarded and exposed to capture

"I adjust" what a player says when he wishes to center a piece on its square and not be forced to move it because of the "touch move" rule

horizontally left or right

illegal move moving a piece improperly or leaving the king in check after making a move

insufficient not enough

insufficient mating material when a player does not have enough material left on the board to force checkmate

isolated passed pawn a pawn that has the weakness of being isolated and the strength of being passed

isolated pawn a weak pawn that cannot be protected by a pawn on a file next to it

interpose to block or put in between

king (symbol – K) the most valuable piece that cannot be captured and moves one square at a time in any direction

kingside the side of the board where the kings begin the game (the e-, f-, g-, and h-files)

knight (symbol – N) worth three pawns and the only piece that can jump over other pieces, moving in the shape of a capital "L"

"knight on the rim is dim" a chess rhyme saying a knight is poorly placed on the edge of the board due to its limited short-range powers

major pieces rooks and queens

mate another word for checkmate

material the sum of the values of the pieces

mating material having enough material to force checkmate

mating net when the king's flight squares are eliminated, making checkmate possible

middlegame the middle part of the game after the pieces have been developed, usually beginning around move ten and lasting until only a few pieces remain on the board

minor pieces knights and bishops

open file a file not blocked by any pawns

opening the first ten or so moves of the game when most of the pieces are developed and the kings castle

passed pawn a pawn that can move all the way up the board to its promotion square without being blocked or captured by an enemy pawn

passive holding back

pawn (symbol – left blank) the least valuable piece on the board that can only move in a forward direction, captures diagonally, and can promote to another piece, usually the queen, when it reaches the other side of the board

pawn chain pawns on files next to each other that are connected in a diagonal line, so they protect each other

perpetual never ending or repeating forever

perpetual check the most common type of three-move repetition, when the player who is usually losing the game forces a position where he can check the other king back and forth forever

pieces knights, bishops, rooks, queens, or kings (pawns are referred to as pawns)

pin when a long-range piece (queen, rook, or bishop) attacks an opponent's piece that is shielding another piece of greater value

promotion or **promoting a pawn** when a pawn gets across the board to the eighth rank and turns into another piece, usually a queen

protected when a piece is defended by a another piece, usually making it a bad idea for the opponent to capture it

protected passed pawn a passed pawn that is protected by a friendly pawn

queen (symbol – Q) the most powerful piece on the board that moves in any direction in a straight line until it runs into another piece or the edge of the board and is worth nine pawns

queenside the side of the board where the queens begin the game (the a-, b-, c-, and d-files)

ranks the chess name for rows that run horizontally across a chess board

resigning when a player loses the game by giving up

roller a type of checkmate where a rook and queen (or two rooks or two queens) take turns moving past each other in order to shrink the box around the opposing king, eventually leading to checkmate

rook (symbol – R) the piece worth five pawns that moves up and down and left and right until it runs into another piece or the edge of the board

sacrifice giving up material in order to gain some other type of advantage or a checkmate

scholastic tournament a chess tournament for children

Scholar's Mate (also known as the four-move checkmate) a quick, easily avoided checkmate where one player wins by bringing his queen out early in the game

score sheet a special piece of paper with spaces for usually 60 moves for each player to record a chess game

skewer a type of tactic like a pin, but where the more valuable piece is in front of the less valuable piece

smothered mate when the king is checkmated by a knight while surrounded by his own pieces (usually a rook and two pawns) which prevent his escape

square of the pawn an imaginary square the defending king must get into in order to win the race to the promotion square with a pawn

stalemate a type of draw where the player to move has no legal moves

starting position the beginning of the game with White to move

sufficient enough

symmetrical mirror image

tactics immediate threats and attacks that make up the battles between pieces

three-move repetition a type of draw that occurs when the same identical position repeats three different times

tempo a single move, relating to time

threat an aggressive move that attacks an opposing piece

"touch move" rule if a player touches his piece, he must move it, if he can legally

"touch take" rule if a player touches an opponent's piece, he must capture it, if he can legally

tripled isolated pawns three pawns lined up vertically on the same file with no pawn on a file next to them to provide protection

tripled pawns three pawns lined up vertically on the same file with a pawn on a file next to them that can provide protection

vertically up or down

White player with the light-colored pieces who moves first in the game

White move written in algebraic notation by giving the move number, followed by a period, and then the move; for example, 15.Nf3

INDEX

ABOUT THE AUTHOR

At age six, Todd Bardwick learned how to play chess from his father, Alan, an expert strength tournament player. Alan utilized many of the chess teaching ideas presented in this book.

Back in the early 1970's when few children played in rated tournaments, Todd consistently improved his game and was nationally ranked most of his youth for his age group.

After leading his high school chess team to several state titles, Todd went to college and graduated first in his class from the University of Colorado at Boulder in 1985 with a B.S. in Civil Engineering. After college, he moved to San Diego for five years where he worked as a rocket scientist (structural analyst).

Moving back to Denver in late 1989, Todd worked as an entrepreneur and continued his chess-playing career. In 1993, Todd achieved the National Master title awarded by the United States Chess Federation (USCF).

Of Todd's numerous tournament achievements, most notable is being the only player to ever win the Denver Open Championship for five consecutive years (1992-1996).

In the early 1990's, Todd discovered his passion for teaching chess to adults and children.

In 1993, he began writing his popular monthly chess column that continues to this day in the Rocky Mountain News, one of the nation's largest newspapers.

In 1995, Todd founded the annual Rocky Mountain Chess camp which has grown to become one of the largest chess camps in the United States. Students come from across the nation to participate in the camp.

In 2002, "The Chess Detective" column was born in School Mates, the national children's chess magazine published by the USCF. In 2003, "The Chess Detective" moved to Chess Life, the United States Chess Federation's adult and children's magazine. Visit www.ColoradoMasterChess.com to see additional columns that Todd has written for the Colorado Chess Informant.

For many years now, Todd has been one of the country's leading full-time chess-teaching masters. His logical and fun approach to the game and reputation as an excellent teacher has inspired Todd to form the Chess Academy of Denver where he teaches well over 750 students per year through private lessons, school classes, chess camps, and year-round camp workshops for adults and children. Todd also regularly trains elementary school teachers who want to learn how to incorporate chess and its educational benefits into their classrooms.

Educationally, Todd runs school district chess programs, teaches in Gifted and Talented programs, and trains parents and teachers how to effectively teach chess to children in their school enrichment programs. Todd accepted an invitation to speak at the 2002 National Gifted and Talented conference for teachers and parents about the benefits of chess and how to improve a child's math skills using chess as a vehicle.

In 2004, Todd completed his first book, *Teaching Chess in the 21st Century – Strategies and Connections to a Standards-Based World*, a comprehensive guide to teaching chess as part of the elementary school math curriculum. The success of *Teaching Chess in the 21st Century* prompted Todd to create this companion workbook.

Todd's students have achieved accolades in life and chess. Successes include gaining early admission to top universities, like Stanford and Yale, becoming Presidential Scholars, being ranked number one in chess in the United States for their age group and winning state and national chess titles.

Todd is available for speaking engagements, chess teacher training, chess lessons, chess classes, and simultaneous chess exhibitions. Todd can be reached through his website at www.ColoradoMasterChess.com.